BIRDS
IN THE GARDEN

BIRDS
IN THE GARDEN

MIKE MOCKLER

BLANDFORD

Blandford Press
An imprint of Cassell plc
Artillery House
Artillery Row
London SW1P 1RT

First published in hardback 1982
First paperback edition 1989

Distributed in the United States by
Sterling Publishing Co. Inc.
2 Park Avenue, New York, NY 10016

Distributed in Australia by
Capricorn Link (Australia) Pty Ltd
PO Box 665, Lane Cove, NSW 2066

ISBN 0-7137-2119-7

British Library Cataloguing in Publication Data
Mockler, Michael
    Birds in the garden.
    1. Birds – Great Britain   2. Garden fauna –
    Great Britain
    1. Title
    598.29′41   QL690.G7

Designed by Logos Design

Printed and bound in Singapore by Toppan Printing Co. (S)

CONTENTS

ACKNOWLEDGEMENTS

I am most grateful to many friends and acquaintances who have assisted with this book in different ways. Some are keen and experienced ornithologists, others merely owners of gardens who have a general interest in the birds that visit them. Together they total several dozen people who have shared anecdotes, experiences, theories and observations with me. Thanks are also due to the Royal Society for the Protection of Birds for helpful information. Various garden-owners, land-owners and farmers have allowed me access to their property for study and photography, and have never complained when my hides and feeding stations have cluttered up their property, often for weeks at a time. In this respect, I am particularly grateful to Mr Bill Edwards, Mr T. Dampney, Mr C. Korbutt, Mr H. Longhurst and Gerry and Ann Cadman.

Most of all, however, I owe a debt of gratitude to my wife, whose patience only occasionally runs short when I sit for hours watching the birds in the garden or spend even longer in a hide attempting to photograph them. I am immensely grateful to her for the many times she has 'walked away' from a hide, helped me to carry bulky photographic equipment and assisted me with countless nest-boxes. Not least, she has checked, amended and typed most of the manuscript for this book, which is dedicated to her.

INTRODUCTION

People who live in towns are often surprised when they learn how many different species of birds can be seen within quite a short distance of where they live. They may be familiar with the common town residents: the feral pigeons and house sparrows that take breadcrumbs from the hand in the local park; the starlings that swarm over lawns and bird-tables; and they may occasionally notice a robin, blackbird or blue tit hopping across a flower bed or flitting through a shrubbery. To the casual observer it may appear that these birds represent the sum total of a town's bird population, but the picture really is very different. In fact, many towns, with their various parks, commons, copses and suburban gardens, boast bird populations, over an entire year, to rival many rural habitats.

To some birds, a town existence actually offers a number of advantages. There is food, for example, which man provides in abundance, either unwittingly, as at refuse tips, or intentionally at the bird-table. A growing interest in natural history in general, and bird life in particular, combined with greater affluence, has resulted in more 'left-overs', not to mention proprietary bird foods, being put out for the birds.

Some of the 'garden regulars' take advantage of this ready and easy supply of food throughout the autumn and winter. Indeed, garden birds such as robins and blackbirds often weigh more in winter than their rural counterparts, and consequently have a better chance of survival. Other species, however, such as some of the finches, are common at bird-tables only if the natural food supply of seeds and berries disappears later in winter. In very cold weather, still more birds come into town gardens in search of food, some of which only turn to man for food as a last desperate measure. Whatever the circumstances, however, the provision of food is useful and beneficial to many birds, and can on occasions mean the difference between life and death.

Another advantage in towns is that the temperature is usually a degree or two higher than in open country: snow cover may be less deep, frozen ground less hard, and life, therefore, slightly easier for ground-feeding birds such as dunnocks, blackbirds and thrushes. In prolonged Arctic spells, redwings and fieldfares have been seen feeding on the grass verges alongside busy suburban roads where they have been able to probe the earth for food, whereas in more exposed rural areas the ground was quite impenetrable.

At night, slightly higher temperatures can be a crucial factor in survival and some birds find sheltered night-time roosts on walls and ledges, and some buildings, with central heating systems, ventilator shafts and warm chimneys, offer additional warmth.

In cold weather, several less familiar species may be seen in towns and gardens. Redwings and mistle thrushes, for example, are driven to roam far afield in search of food when the ground is frozen or covered with snow.

In many respects, life in a town or suburban garden is probably safer too. Despite prowling cats, the increasingly urban fox, the presence of kestrels, sparrowhawks and tawny owls (as well as man with his motor cars, air-guns and poisonous chemicals), there are still fewer predators and dangers in towns and gardens than in most country districts. In fact, towns, with their parks and gardens, can offer all that many birds require: security, shelter, roosts, nest-sites and food. An inspection of the lay-out of a town will reveal a greater diversity of habitats—and, therefore, a wider variety of birds—than earth-bound man might expect to find.

TOWN CENTRE AND SUBURBS

In the very centre of a town or city, there are few private gardens and living accommodation is limited, in the main, to old blocks of flats and tenements. The dominant buildings are large

A surprising variety of birds may be seen in a town. Many find cover, food and nest-sites in parks and gardens; some frequent areas of water; others follow a belt of trees or a river, or they may visit from neighbouring fields.

offices, department stores, warehouses and multi-storey car parks, with a scattering of other large buildings, such as hospitals, railway stations, hotels, cinemas and churches.

In such a habitat, the bird population is extremely limited; there are feral pigeons, house sparrows and starlings, with the possibility of pied wagtails, black-headed gulls and perhaps the odd blackbird or kestrel. If the air is clean enough to provide a supply of flying insects, and if there are suitable nest-sites, swifts and house martins may be seen in summer. What makes the picture more interesting, however, is that there will probably be many other birds in the area if there is a park or some other pocket of greenery nearby.

A little further from the centre, there is likely to be a ring of high-density housing, consisting often of terraced houses, built before the turn of the century, where the majority of gardens are small and rather bare of trees and shrubs. Here there may be a few dunnocks, robins, and collared doves, as well as the town-dwelling birds already mentioned. In larger gardens, song thrush, blue and great tit, woodpigeon and greenfinch might be added to the list.

The size and age of the town will determine how quickly this kind of housing gives way to the familiar older suburban arrangement: usually semi-detached houses with small front gardens, enclosed by privet hedges and low brick walls, and quite large established rear gardens containing mature fruit trees, flower beds and vegetable patches. Here the bird population will be larger: those species already mentioned will be more abundant, and others like wren, mistle thrush, magpie, crow, jackdaw, goldfinch, chaffinch and bullfinch may be seen as well. Migrating willow warblers and chiffchaffs also sometimes pay fleeting visits in spring and late summer.

Moving further out, we enter the more wooded suburbs with tall, mature trees, including oak, chestnut, beech and silver birch. Here there are gardens with sufficient shrubs and bushes to provide ample nest-sites for several species and it is here that one can hope to see some of the birds more normally associated with woods. Coal tit, long-tailed tit, marsh tit, nuthatch, green and great spotted woodpeckers, jay and goldcrest may be present at any time of the year; and siskins, bramblings, blackcaps and redpolls will possibly make winter appearances. In certain parts of Britain, such suburbs might have resident treecreepers, lesser spotted woodpeckers, tree sparrows and sparrowhawks, while during migration, redstarts, pied flycatchers, spotted flycatchers, blackcaps, garden warblers, whitethroats, lesser whitethroats, willow warblers and chiffchaffs will pass through, and may even stay to breed.

There are countless other types of housing, of course, which this cursory survey has ignored. One of the most familiar is the modern, open-plan estate. Here the front gardens are small, and tend to be featureless; rear gardens are usually almost as small, with lawns and flower beds vastly outnumbering trees and shrubs, and enclosed by walls or fencing rather than hedges. Here the trees and shrubs are likely to be ornamental and foreign varieties which offer no cover or nest-sites, and the bird populations in these areas are often as narrow and lacking in variety as many city centres.

URBAN SANCTUARIES

Fortunately, only a short distance away from most gardens there are pockets of greenery such as pleasure gardens and botanical gardens, some of which can boast as varied a bird life as many areas of rural woodland. In some of the London parks, for example, a hundred or more species are recorded in most years, up to half of which breed successfully, though in many town parks the bird life is rather restricted: the human presence is too insistent and pervasive, the habitat more akin to open fields with isolated trees than woodland with clearings. Football pitches and bowling greens, ice-cream kiosks and sports pavilions hardly constitute a valuable habitat for many birds, though, of course, they do serve an important recreational function for the local human populace. Where shrubberies exist, too often they are either small and dissected by countless paths, or they consist of dense, rampant rhododendrons which throttle other vegetation and support virtually no mammal, insect or bird life.

Yet there are enough town parks around the country with a varied bird life to prove that it is possible to have an amenity area for humans which is also a sanctuary for wildlife. In these bird-rich parks there are large groups of mature trees, which almost comprise small woods; within them are dense thickets of undergrowth, with brambles, hawthorn, nettles and tall grasses (which, unlike rhododendrons, allow light to enter and support a rich web of life). Here birds thrive and humans only occasionally intrude. Native trees and bushes outnumber exotic ornamental species and dead timber is not regarded as unsightly but, instead, is allowed to stand to

A study of a town or city from the air reveals a number of 'urban sanctuaries' for birds: parks, gardens, wooded churchyards and tree-lined avenues. A variety of birds use these pockets of greenery on passage to rest and feed; other birds such as the blue tit above breed there and spread out to the neighbouring gardens when the breeding season is over.

provide food and potential nest-sites for tree-creepers, woodpeckers, nuthatches and tits.

Other small urban areas can also serve as bird sanctuaries. Church yards, particularly if they are slightly untidy and overgrown, contain bushes and thickets which support insect life and offer nest-sites. Uncut grasses, weeds and flowers produce seeds for finches and other seed-eaters. There are often yews and other conifers which permit coal tits and goldcrests to flourish and, if there are several old deciduous trees, as is often the case, there may be a small population of tits and even woodpeckers.

Small secluded corners like this are easily overlooked by humans but they are of immense value to numerous birds. Many older schools, hospitals and municipal buildings stand in grounds that are well stocked with trees and bushes. Canals, rivers, roads, railway lines, quarries and allotments are often lined with weeds and scrub, where sallow, birch, hawthorn, blackthorn, brambles, and nettles may grow. Indeed, disused railway tracks have long been recognised as potential nature reserves. Elsewhere there are patches of industrial wasteland such as unkempt scrap metal yards, derelict factories and docks, and overgrown goods yards where weeds like plantains, dock, dandelion, groundsel and rosebay willowherb quickly develop to provide food for flocks of finches, particularly goldfinches.

Building plots, awaiting development, become overgrown with bushes and brambles where birds can nest, and in most towns there are commons, spinneys and copses tucked away, some of them belonging to the council, others apparently forgotten by whoever owns them.

Sadly, the way in which these sites are abused by vandalism and the tipping of rubbish is all too familiar. There is no shortage of developers and speculators who see the value of such places in economical terms only so that these valuable pockets of woodland are nibbled away at the edges until they become worthless in ornithological terms.

Further out into the suburbs, where town merges into farmland and countryside, there are other green oases: market gardens and nurseries, sports grounds and golf courses, orchards and paddocks. There are also reservoirs, flooded gravel pits and sewage works where quite different birds thrive: gulls, swans, geese, ducks, moorhens, grebes, herons and miscellaneous waterside birds.

As well as serving as invaluable havens for resident birds, these 'islands' have an important role in aiding the movements of birds into, around and through an urban landscape. Migrating birds, like willow warblers, chiffchaffs and spotted flycatchers, often work their way along a line of trees, feeding as they travel. Many other birds follow the line of a river or some other prominent topographical feature. Tree-lined rivers, canals, railway lines and parks thus drive a wedge into a built-up area and offer birds the opportunity of moving into a town relatively easily. At the same time, other, non-migratory birds have the chance to move freely from one locality to another possibly to colonise other suburbs and parks. If pockets of woodland and parks are not too isolated, they can serve an important function as 'stepping stones' for those species, such as some of the more typical woodland birds, for instance woodpeckers, nuthatch, long-tailed tit and marsh tit, which are reluctant to venture far from a park or copse.

If areas of water are not too far off, herons and kingfishers, mallards and moorhens may find their way to the garden, as well as reed buntings and grey wagtails. A heron is quite likely to spot a garden pond as it flaps slowly on its huge wings high above suburbia, in transit from one river or pond to another. In some areas, owners of garden ponds are driven to placing nets over their ponds to protect their ornamental fish from attack. For many, however, the metre-tall grey sentinel standing, spectre-like and still, beside the garden pond would be a welcome sight, for which they would be only too willing to sacrifice a few goldfish. For a kingfisher to locate the pond is rather more difficult as it does not normally fly high above the ground, or water; nevertheless it will visit gardens which are not far from a river, lake or pond.

Not all birds which visit gardens and bird-tables need these so-called 'stepping stones' to aid their journey. Indeed, some like collared doves, starlings, house sparrows, jackdaws and pied wagtails are as likely to be seen perching on television aerials, street lamps, fences and power cables as in trees. Starlings tour around above an area of housing and swarm down onto lawns, playing fields and bird-tables. Gulls behave in a similar way, swooping down to pluck food from a garden, and swifts, swallows and house martins have no use at all for trees and bushes. Other birds which enter areas of a town and gardens which are rather devoid of trees are the species more typical of open country rather than those that were originally woodland birds. For example, goldfinches and, to a lesser extent, greenfinches, have a remarkable knack of spotting food in a weedy flower bed as they flit past overhead.

So we see that towns and gardens are different things to different birds, but, no matter how they use them, the birds are there, sometimes in considerable numbers: one just has to learn to notice them—to train the eye and, what is often even more important, the ear, to locate them. A Christmas shopping expedition to the centre of a medium-sized town in southern England was once enlivened for me firstly by the tutting calls of some long-tailed tits which drew my attention to a party of these delightful birds flitting with whirring wings, in twos and threes between buses and lorries as they crossed from the town's pleasure gardens to a large shrub-filled traffic island in the middle of the shopping centre. Soon after, nearby, the distinctive, sharp call of a great spotted woodpecker was heard and eventually a fine male bird was sighted, high up in a dead silver birch overhanging the road. A short time later, at the same spot, a female sparrowhawk sped across the road, dashing low to the ground between moving cars, before disappearing into the trees in the nearby gardens.

VERSATILITY: ADAPTATION AND REGIONAL VARIATION

A day's birdwatching one October produced a list of species identified that included blackbird, mistle thrush, woodpigeon, robin, goldfinch, greenfinch, chaffinch, great spotted woodpecker, green woodpecker, carrion crow, magpie, jay, starling and house sparrow. All of these birds are common in many suburban areas of Britain, so the list may not seem particularly interesting, until, that is, one learns that the day in question was spent in the high sierras of southern Spain!

This is mentioned because it serves to illustrate two points. The first is that there is no such thing as a garden bird. No bird was designed by nature, so to speak, to inhabit gardens in the way that it can be said that other birds, such as water birds or sea birds, are perfectly adapted for a life in their particular habitats. A garden is not a natural habitat but something which has been imposed on the landscape by man. Because it resembles a number of different habitats, scrub, hedgerow and woodland, for example, a variety of birds have learned to survive there. This brings us to the second point: those birds which have been able to survive in the environment that urban man has created have done so because of their extraordinary versatility.

The birds that are the subject of this book, then, are, for the most part, the survivors: tough, resilient and inventive. Many of them have come to trust man; some merely to disregard him; some show remarkable ingenuity in taking advantage of life in the modern world. Tits peck open milk bottle tops to drink the cream, starlings, sparrows, even swifts, use oddments like string and paper for their nests, jackdaws make nests in chimneys, black-headed gulls wait in lay-bys and car parks for scraps to be thrown to them and many birds feed well on council rubbish tips.

There is enormous variation, however, between individuals in different regions and, even

The bird-table in this small garden attracts woodpeckers, nuthatches and treecreepers from the nearby woodland in winter. Fruit bushes provide food for blackcaps and other warblers in late summer. Evergreen bushes and hedges offer nest-sites to goldcrests, finches and thrushes.

more so, in different countries. The robin is a good example. In a British garden it is likely to be so tame that the gardener must take care not to tread on the bird while he is digging his garden. By contrast, but understandably, in several European countries, where it has been shot and trapped, it is a shy and timid bird of woodland thickets.

It is because birds are so variable in their behaviour that I have approached with trepidation the matter of deciding which species to include in and which to omit from a book such as this. Changes are taking place all the time and make it extremely difficult to draw hard and fast distinctions. The point has already been made that there is really no such thing as a garden bird.

To take an extreme example, the red kite is one of the rarest birds of prey in Britain, with only a few embattled pairs surviving, under heavy protection, in the hilly parts of central Wales. No one would expect this splendid bird to be considered in a book about garden or town birds, yet the red kite was an extremely common scavenger amongst the rubbish and rotting waste of Shakespeare's England. Until it was blasted almost into oblivion by gamekeepers in the first half of the nineteenth century, this beautiful raptor was probably as familiar to town dwellers as the carrion crow is today.

Over a similar period of time the blackbird has made progress in the opposite direction. Eric Simms, in *British Thrushes*, makes the interesting observation that Gilbert White, writing in the eighteenth century, barely mentions the blackbird, and that this bird was not known as a breeding bird around man's habitation before the second half of the nineteenth century. Before the 1950s, collared doves were never seen in Britain. Yet, today, there cannot be a town in the kingdom which does not have a breeding population of these birds.

Other changes have taken place, some spectacular, some less so, and more are still occurring. Magpies are becoming increasingly common in suburbs, just as song thrushes, in some areas, are seen less often, an exchange that few people would find appealing. A recent survey by the British Trust for Ornithology has recorded a lesser spotted woodpecker feeding on a peanut holder and a kingfisher hovering at a scrap basket. In another garden, a treecreeper became a bird-table regular and a lesser redpoll hung onto the nut basket and successfully extracted peanuts.

Is there going to be another species, like the collared dove, which today is never seen in Britain but which will be a common sight in towns and suburbs by the year 2000? Or perhaps there will be one that is already occasionally seen in British towns or gardens that will change its habits or expand its population. Could it be either the redstart or the black redstart? There is no obvious reason why either of these two small birds should not be more frequent during the summer in the towns and gardens of Britain. The redstart is neither scarce nor afraid of man and has been a breeding bird of the suburbs in the past. In a few parts of Britain it is so prolific that it is just about the most prominent bird and in such places it shows a willingness to share man's dwellings. In France, Belgium and Switzerland, the redstart shows a robin-like predilection for bizarre nest-sites—old kettles and tins, disused vehicles, machinery and gaps under roofs of buildings, and in Germany it is called *Gartenrotschwanz* ('garden redtail'). The black redstart, though so rare in Britain that it merits special protection by law, is as common and tame in towns and villages in some European countries as any British robin. In Germany, it is so closely associated with man's buildings that it is known as *Hausrotschwanz*—the 'house redtail'.

In the face of so many changes and inexplicable aberrations it is a relief to learn that some things apparently do not change. In 1825, the poet John Clare wrote the following in his notes:
'. . . the Robin seems to be fond of the company and haunts of man it builds its nest close to his cottage . . . nay it will even settle on the gardeners spade when he is at work to watch the worm that he throws up and unbears and in winter it will venture into the house for food . . .'

CHAPTER 1

DAY AND NIGHT

THE ROLE OF FEATHERS

The possession of feathers distinguishes a bird from all other creatures on earth. Feathers are also extraordinarily versatile, functional and vital to the bird's survival in many respects.

Firstly, of course, feathers provide a bird with the means of flight, with the exception of a few non-British species such as ostrich and emu. Flight often provides a means of escape from a predator. It also offers birds great freedom of movement so that they can travel relatively quickly in search of food. In bad weather or in times of food shortage, they can move to another area or another country where the food supply is more plentiful. For many of our birds this involves huge distances in spring and autumn migration.

Large birds such as eagles and vultures and some other birds of prey have broad, sail-like wings for soaring high above the ground to locate food. By contrast, a tiny humming bird's wings can move so fast that they are a blur to the human eye. There are even birds which can use their wings to swim or 'fly' under water.

Of the garden species, the majority have 'general purpose' wing-designs, for most are non-specialist fliers. A few birds, however, have evolved specialised wing-shapes, which in most cases assist them in their quest for food. Swallows, house martins and swifts catch their food, in the form of flying insects, in mid-air and with their slim, sharply pointed wings they are able to fly extremely fast in pursuit of their prey. A falcon, such as a kestrel, also relies on direct and rapid flight to obtain food so its wings are long and pointed too. The sparrowhawk uses a hunting technique which involves short, sudden bursts of flight round, and between, trees, hedges and buildings, its sudden appearance taking unwary small birds by surprise. In such circumstances, abrupt twists, turns and changes of direction are necessary so a hawk's wings are shorter and more rounded.

Tail feathers are also important. The swallow's long tail-streamers assist its streamlined flight as do the forked tails of house martin and swift. Even among garden birds with 'standard' tail designs, tail feathers are used for steering, balance and

Feathers are very versatile and even tail feathers can be put to different uses. A few species possess specially designed tails to provide support but even some of those that do not, like this redstart, can improvise, if necessary.

braking. Although this is not often easy to see with the smaller garden birds, close observation at a bird-table of some species, such as great tit and chaffinch, which both have striking white outer tail feathers, will reveal the amount to which tail feathers are used in flight. With large birds, it is sometimes possible to see the tail being tilted like a rudder.

For birds which cling to the sides of tree trunks, the tail serves yet another purpose. A woodpecker's central tail feathers are especially stiff and strong so that they act as a brace or support. A woodpecker always presses its tail against the side of the tree to which it is clinging so that, with the two feet, a tripod is formed. A treecreeper also possesses stiff tail feathers and uses them in an

In cold weather, feathers provide valuable insulation and may mean the difference between life and death. By puffing out its body feathers, this mistle thrush has trapped a layer of air underneath, thus maintaining body heat.

identical way, although the nuthatch, which also works its way up and down tree trunks, has evolved exceedingly strong claws rather than a long tail for this purpose. Even birds, such as some tits, redstarts and pied flycatchers, which do not possess tails designed for this purpose, will press their tails hard against a tree trunk or nest-box if they have to hold on to the side of it.

The wings and tails provide the means of flight so it is not surprising that the feathers there are the largest and strongest. Though these feathers are long and quite stiff, they are surprisingly flexible and hard-wearing. They are certainly not hard, brittle or fragile. Just as important, however, are the soft and delicate body feathers and, beneath them, the greyish down feathers which provide the necessary insulation in cold conditions and maintain the bird's body temperature. A fat-looking bird in the garden in severe winter weather is not well-fed and overweight; in fact, the opposite is likely to be the case. The rotund appearance is probably caused by the puffing out of the body feathers causing air to be trapped

beneath, next to the bird's body. The air then warms to body temperature and serves as a second skin.

There is another type of feather which, because it has no web and consists only of a fine quill, looks more like a hair. These delicate feathers are sensitive to touch, like an animal's whiskers, and can be seen growing in small clusters around the base of the bill on many of the garden birds.

For some birds, the colour of the plumage provides a degree of concealment. As we will see later, young birds which have recently left the nest often have dull, mottled markings to afford them added protection at a time when they are very vulnerable. Some adults which have to incubate in a relatively open nest have dark or drab backs compared to colourful or light breasts and underparts. Robin and thrushes spring to mind immediately. Other species, such as willow warbler and chiffchaff which spend most of their time perching and foraging among the foliage of trees, have yellow and buff-green markings so that they blend in extremely well with the leaves. In the case of one bird at least a pattern of behaviour has developed specifically to utilise the cryptic coloration of its plumage. When danger threatens, a treecreeper will press itself close to the trunk of the tree upon which it is perched, hiding any of the creamy-white breast and flank feathers. The mottled brown back enables the bird, when it remains motionless in such a position, to become almost part of the bark.

Feathers, especially the most striking and colourful ones, are an important feature of a bird's social life and are used by the bird in a variety of situations to give signals to others of its own kind.

An obvious example among garden birds is the robin, which threatens a rival by puffing out its red breast feathers to draw attention to them. If the intruder is perched above, then the head has to be thrown back and the chest thrust upwards so that the largest possible expanse of red is pointing towards the enemy. If the rival is at a lower level the red breast is puffed out downwards. While threatening, the robin often cocks its tail and flicks its wings, and may raise its crown feathers. The robin is the most fiercely

For the robin, the red breast feathers are important to express aggression: they are puffed out towards a rival amid bursts of singing.

territorial of all the garden birds and even a bundle of red robin breast feathers will prompt an attack.

Although, for the robin, the red feathers feature only in acts of aggression, for other birds colour may be associated with sexual behaviour. In many cases, certain colourful feathers are a prominent part of both threat and sexual display. The cock chaffinch highlights his white wing flashes for the benefit of an enemy and he also draws attention to them when posturing before a female. In this sexual display, he turns sideways on towards her and tilts his body to show off his red flanks. Red is also prominent in a goldfinch's sexual display when both birds puff out the scarlet blazes on their faces, at the same time swaying

from side to side and drawing attention to the gold feathers on the wing. As a pair of great spotted woodpeckers chase each other around the tree trunks and branches in spring, the bright crimson under-tail coverts of each bird are clearly visible to the other.

For the redstart, red is not associated with aggression at all; in fact, it has been found that this species finds the colour attractive and will sometimes pick up red objects. The red tail also features strongly in courtship and the choice of a nest hole. In sexual chases the red tails of both birds are fanned out very strikingly, and the male redstart tries to attract his female to build in a hole or nest-box by flying in and out of the hole several times in very quick succession, thus displaying his red rump and tail. He may also glide down to the hole with wings and red tail spread. When inside the hole, he will look out at the hen so that the white patch on his otherwise black head is extremely conspicuous. 'Nest-invitation' displays like this are not uncommon. The male pied fly-catcher nips in and out of the hole or nest-box, frequently pausing to hang on the outside, revealing his white wing bars. The cock wren lacks any bright colours, but he shows the female his 'cock's nests' by flying towards them and shivering his wings. The cock house sparrow attempts to attract a female to his nest-site by sitting in it and quivering his wings.

In sexual display the cock siskin raises his black crown and bright lemon rump feathers, while the greenfinch lowers his wings to show off his yellow rump and the bright yellow feathers on wings and tail. The predominantly yellow crown of the male goldcrest includes a few orange feathers, which are usually concealed underneath the yellow. In threat and courtship the crown is raised to reveal these orange feathers. In its sexual display, too, the cock nuthatch puffs out its body feathers, so drawing attention to his bright chestnut-coloured flanks. The tail is also spread out to display the white feathers.

There are some other species amongst which the colour of the rump and tail would appear to be significant. The white rumps of the house martin and brambling probably serve as an important signal when on migration, telling the bird immediately behind to follow. Thus it is a means whereby the migrating flock can be held together.

For a flock of finches feeding on a lawn or at a bird-table, the brighter feathers can provide other messages. A flock of chaffinches feeding on the ground would be clearly visible from above because of their white shoulder patches. Other birds flying overhead would know that food was available there and drop down to join those on the ground. If danger threatens, on the other hand, one bird will suddenly fly up showing its bright wing-bars and tail feathers. The rest of the flock can instantly follow suit and dive towards cover or fly off.

In the case of many species, sexual display (*see also* Chapter 2) contains elements of aggression, and in some cases the two types of behaviour may be so similar as to be indistinguishable. A blue tit, for example, will raise its blue crown feathers when excited or agitated and may be seen doing so during courtship as well as when threatening a rival for its territory or food supply. It is often possible, in fact, to see aspects of aggression around a bird-table where birds such as tits squabble over peanuts and scraps. The threat posture of the great tit is quite striking: the tail is fanned, and the wing feathers spread wide to reveal the black and yellow chest.

Generally speaking, birds avoid physical battle if possible. The visual displays are usually sufficient warning to one of the antagonists for it to beat a retreat; they are, like song and some calls, a ritualised alternative to actual fighting.

DAILY CARE OF FEATHERS

Because feathers are used in so many ways, and are indispensable for a bird's survival, great attention is paid to their care and maintenance. Birds in gardens can often be observed tending to their plumage; the most common activity is preening. In towns, in particular, birds can become extremely grimy; on sparrows and light-coloured birds, such as woodpigeons, the dirt is quite visible. Also, when feeding young, a parent bird's feathers do not receive as much attention as at other times of the year and, for hole-nesters, the feathers may be the subject of terrific wear and tear as the bird goes in and out of the nest-hole.

Preening for many birds involves the use of the preen gland, which is located near the point where the tail feathers join the body. This gland secretes a fluid which serves as a 'conditioner' for the feathers, ensuring that they retain their insulation and waterproofing and remain strong and supple. Inexperienced observers watching a bird preening are sometimes puzzled by the way the bird returns several times to the area of the body where that gland is situated and assume that there is a troublesome feather or some irritation there. What the bird is doing, in fact, is transferring the preen fluid from the gland to the feathers. As the beak passes along each feather a small quantity of the fluid is spread over it. Generally speaking, however, the preen gland is far less important to a garden bird than to an aquatic bird for whom waterproofing is essential, and some clean their feathers without using the gland at all. The passage of the beak, with or with-

out preen fluid, tidies up the ruffled feathers, many of which have a web or vane, consisting of barbs and barbules which interlock like the teeth of a zip to give an airtight and watertight surface. The passage of the beak has a similar effect to the closing of a zip. Careful observation will reveal that a different feather or group of feathers is serviced each time.

Preening is frequently accompanied by head-scratching, which apart from easing an irritation may also transfer preen oil from the preen gland to the head: the claw takes the oil from the bill to the head feathers; then the bird rolls its head onto its back, transferring some of the fluid from the head to those feathers on its upper back which cannot be reached with the beak. Most passerines scratch their heads by lowering a wing and bringing the leg on that side forward and over the wing, an action which can be tricky, especially for a young bird which may topple forward. The preening often ends with the bird having a thorough shake to get rid of loose dirt and parasites.

Another key factor in the bird's toiletry is bathing, which may be observed at any time of the year, even in deepest winter when the ground is frozen hard. Winter is the time of year when feathers most need to be in good condition. When food is difficult to come by, considerable time and energy may be wasted in foraging, and protection from the cold is even more important. Most birds bathe by lowering their breasts into the water, dipping their heads in and tossing water backwards over their body. The tail is also submerged and the wings flap to flick water over the back. Some birds, like thrushes and willow warbler, may bathe in grass wet from rain or dew; some, such as magpies and crows, have been observed bathing in rain and even snow. Again the wings are constantly flicked to spread the moisture through the feathers.

Feathers are crucial to a bird's survival, so time must be spent each day caring for them. A tree sparrow (above) preens its wing feathers and a bullfinch (below) bathes in a pond, using its wing to flick water up over its back.

Two other types of feather care are less commonly seen but do occur from time to time in gardens. The first is dust-bathing, in which the bird manipulates the particles of dust or soil much as it would the droplets of water, and achieves much the same effect. The dust-particles clean off dirt and parasites from the feathers—just as it is possible to remove grease from one's hands by rubbing them in sand. House sparrows are particularly fond of this method and groups of them can often be seen dust-bathing in dry gutters, flower beds and sand pits.

The second method is seen far less frequently. Ants, when annoyed, squirt a small quantity of formic acid. Some birds have found that this substance will disturb noisome parasites and enable the bird to rid itself of them. A limited number of birds habitually indulge in 'anting', as it is called, but over 200 species have been recorded making use of it. The jay is the most frequent 'anter', and may perform this action every two or three days. Others, such as thrushes, starlings, rooks and magpies, do so occasionally. The bird appears to gain considerable pleasure from the experience and may show something akin to ecstasy, going into a trance or stupor.

Anting exists in two forms: in the first, the bird merely squats over an ants' nest, permitting the ants to crawl around in the feathers squirting formic acid; in the second, the bird actually picks up an ant in its beak and moves it through the feathers, while the ant angrily squirts formic acid. After anting, the bird will usually take a bath.

An extraordinary variation of anting is sometimes referred to as 'fire-anting'. For crows and rooks fire apparently has a fascination, and they have been known to take away burning material to a nest and to perform an anting ceremony over the smouldering nest. One rook, at least, has been known to lie over burning straw. It would appear that the heat of the fire, like the heat of the sun when birds are 'sunbathing', causes parasites to move.

THE LENGTH OF A BIRD'S DAY

On a bright day, birds will continue feeding longer and will be noticeably later arriving at their roosts than on dull and misty evenings when they fly to their roost far earlier, in some cases by as much as an hour or more. The level of light intensity will also affect the time of leaving the roost in the morning, and the commencement of singing. Furthermore, the pattern of behaviour may alter as a result of the prevailing weather conditions. If it is bright and clear, birds can be seen flying to roost high in the sky. On wet and windy days, most prefer to fly low over the trees and rooftops, where they are less exposed to the buffeting of the wind; so, too, the dusk 'chinking' sessions of blackbirds and evening aerial displays of starlings are cut short.

Some species have shorter hours than others. The house sparrow is one of the last to appear in the morning and one of the first to settle in for the night. The thrushes, conversely, including the blackbird, and their relatives the robin and the two redstarts, have very long days. These birds have relatively large eyes permitting them to see well in the dark, so they can be active and singing before first light and may go on foraging at the end of the day when it is quite dim. In fact, the first bird sound of the day, especially in the winter, is usually the song of the local robin which can sometimes be heard while it is still dark. By comparison, some of the birds which roost in holes, in particular the woodpeckers, are late to rise. It has been suggested that this is as a result of the light taking longer to penetrate their roost-hole, but this may be only a partial explanation as woodpeckers sometimes go to their roost surprisingly early in the evening.

Other features of roosting are probably easier to explain, such as the seasonal variation in roosting times. In winter, the garden birds, although retiring at an early hour by the clock, in fact stay up longer in relation to sunset than they do in summer. Unless feeding young in the nest, they may go to roost well before sunset in the summer months but will go on searching for food after sunset in winter. This is because the days in summer are sufficiently long to allow a bird to feed well and still have time to spare. In the shorter days of winter, it has to use every minute available to find enough food to survive.

In the case of virtually all the garden birds, it is the male which works longer hours, starting his day well before his mate is up and, usually, retiring some time after her. Among some species, such as the wren and house sparrow, the male has even been known to escort his female to her roost before going to his own sleeping quarters! In the case of garden birds defending territories the male needs to be up early, for it is in the early part of the morning that borders are re-established for the day to come. Territorial behaviour is at its most intense at this time—hence the 'dawn chorus' of spring.

GARDEN BIRDS AT NIGHT

Most garden birds sleep on a branch in any bush, hedge or tree which offers protection from the elements and concealment from predators. In summer, this could be almost any vegetation; but in the winter months evergreens are the most popular choice, especially those with fairly large leaves such as rhododendron, laurel, holly and possibly ivy. The perch chosen will probably be some way above the ground, giving the bird a measure of immunity from ground-predators. It is not usually in the upper reaches of a tall tree, as this position would be too exposed to strong winds. A tree or bush in a hollow provides additional protection from the wind.

A bird cannot easily dry off at night, so it is important that it is sheltered from rain and snow even more than from cold winds, otherwise it will lose body heat and possibly die. For this reason the roost-site is often in vegetation close to a wind-break, such as a building or wall. Some birds actually sleep on ledges and crevices on the outsides of buildings, and others even roost inside buildings.

A bird sleeping on a branch is not in danger of falling off, for the weight of the bird's body automatically causes the feet to clasp the perch. The more relaxed the bird is, the tighter the grasp, so it does not need to hold on consciously.

While sleeping, the bird generally has its head turned back so that the beak and face can be tucked under the scapulars, the feathers at the side of the back where the wing meets the body. The legs, like the beak, lack feathering, so are a potential source of heat-loss. Therefore, as the bird presses down on the perch, the body feathers cover the legs, leaving no part without insulation. In addition, a bird can sleep balanced on one leg, permitting each leg in turn to be lifted up deeper into the belly feathers which further reduces the loss of body heat.

The birds which spend the night in holes are mainly those species which also nest in holes. Just as theirs is the safest method of nesting, they are also more secure when roosting. Not only are they sheltered from wind and rain but also most nocturnal predators. The tawny owl, for example, cannot reach them, whereas it can attack birds which spend the night amongst vegetation. This it achieves by striking the branches of the bush or tree in which the birds are gathered, thereby dislodging them from their perches.

Although five species of owl occur regularly in Britain, the only one commonly found in towns is the tawny owl.

Actually, some diurnal predators present probably the biggest threat: birds of prey such as sparrowhawk and kestrel hunt in the half-light of dawn and dusk and are often successful. One kestrel made regular dawn raids on a large, old block of flats in the centre of a town where it launched attacks on departing house sparrows, as well as bats returning after a night's activity. Sparrowhawks are especially shrewd and frequently spring surprise attacks on birds flying into their roosts at the end of the day or leaving in the morning.

A common misconception is that birds use their nests for sleeping in as if they are 'homes'. With the exception of a small number of species, this is not the case, although in the short period when eggs and young are in the nest one or both of the parents sleep there. That is not to say that nests and nest-holes are not used later as roost-sites by the birds which bred in or fledged from them. If this does happen, in most cases, it is because the situation offers good night-time

facilities rather than as a result of any affinity with the place. In fact, a hole-roosting bird can sleep in a tiny space, even a crack in the bark of an old tree, and can comfortably spend the night in a place which could not possibly serve as a nest chamber.

At night, tawny owls hunt, and in the breeding season carry out all the activities associated with a bird's breeding cycle: defining and defending territory, pairing, mating, and bringing up young. They sleep during the day, either in a larger hollow in a tree, which may also be the nest-hole, or close to the trunk on a lateral branch of a large ivy-clad tree, concealed amongst the leaves. Often the best chance of seeing a tawny owl comes when the bird is disturbed from its day-time roost and flies off with strong, silent wing-beats, much to the concern of all other birds in the locality which join together to mob the owl.

There are also a few birds which sing when it is dark. The nightingale, hardly a garden bird in Britain, is the most famous example, singing, day and night, almost without stopping, from the end of April to the end of May or, occasionally, for a short time in early June. At the same time the cuckoo may sing for much of the night. There are some more familiar birds which sing at night: robin, blackbird, dunnock and, occasionally, wren. The presence of street lighting can apparently deceive the bird into thinking that it is day.

Finally, of course, there are birds which spend some nights on the wing. They will only do so when migrating, with the notable exception of the swift which sometimes chooses, even when there are young in the nest, to sleep in the night sky (though the 'sleeping' probably consists of a series of short snoozes while gliding between periodic wing-beats). Sometimes, as dusk falls, a large group of swifts will rise up from their breeding colony and float away out of sight into the gathering gloom.

Birds which are on the move at night can sometimes be heard as they pass overhead. Geese are probably the most well-known example, but some of the thrushes can also be heard calling to each other on night migration flights. On autumn nights, the redwing's 'tzeep' is an evocative and significant sound to ornithologists, telling of the arrival of these winter visitors from the north. In fact, many birds migrate by day and night, if weather permits, for not only is the journey completed more quickly that way but there is also the advantage that the bird can use part of the day for feeding if it wishes.

Autumn and Winter

During the autumn and winter months, many of the birds which visit our gardens have greater mobility than in the breeding season, unrestricted as they are by the demands of a nest or territorial duties. A number of species form themselves into flocks of various sizes which feed together during the day and sleep together at night, whereas others are more independent during the daytime but gather together for the night. A few, mainly those which remain in their territory for the winter, are more or less solitary by both day and night, although some of them change their roosting habits if the weather turns very cold.

Probably the most familiar roosting activity is the evening gathering of starlings. Huge communal roosts occur in many towns and cities, gathering together in great clouds above the streets as the day draws to a close. The process normally begins some time earlier, well away from the roost, as parties of starlings feeding in gardens, parks and surrounding open land join up with other groups in the vicinity. As more and more groups join, the flock is rapidly enlarged and heads towards the roost, still merging with other flocks as it goes. The flight-paths are fairly regular each day so individuals which have become detached earlier can relocate their fellows simply by waiting somewhere along the route.

When the birds arrive at the roost they merge with other similar flocks which have flown in from other directions. They combine in a spectacular aerial display, until they pour downwards in waves to the roost. This may be a clump of large trees or even a single tree, into which the starlings miraculously pack themselves. In city centres, the roost is often a large, older-style building with plenty of ledges upon which the birds can sleep; tall shops, banks and office blocks are often used. Usually these large roosts are used year after year but sometimes they fall into disuse for no apparent reason. In certain cases, this is just as well, because not only do trees and buildings become seriously fouled by all the droppings but the sheer weight of birds can cause branches to break and trees to be permanently damaged or even killed.

Not all the local starlings are drawn into these huge roosts. Those that breed in the area may spend the night in local roosts probably in their own territories and some will actually use their nest-holes as sleeping quarters. Among the locust-like swarms that use the main roosts there are probably many young birds which have not yet settled in a particular territory, as well as many thousands from other areas, including, no doubt, continental immigrants.

The blackbird is another bird which uses social roosts. Not all gardens offer good cover in winter, so many blackbirds fly a short distance, probably no more than one or two kilometres, to spend the night at a communal roost. This may contain no more than ten to twenty birds, but some roosts may be two or three times that size.

The site—in thick bushes, often evergreens such as rhododendron, holly and privet—is usually located in large gardens, parks, copses, churchyards, cemetaries or waste-ground, and is not normally difficult to find. The sight of blackbirds, in ones and twos, diving in fast direct flight in one direction near the end of the day is an obvious clue. The birds fly quite low, darting between moving vehicles and flitting between houses, apparently making little effort to conceal their destination.

It is at these times that they strike up their distinctive autumn and winter evensong, the familiar 'chinking', which they repeat in the morning. With the accompaniment of the singing robin, this forms the 'dawn chorus' during much of the autumn and winter. The significance of this phenomenon has been the subject of much discussion. It is indulged in primarily by dominant, mature birds and territory-holding males, and probably serves to announce the possession of territory, as with song in spring and summer. As the blackbirds move to the communal roost, they trespass on the territories of others causing

the holders of those territories to set up their 'chinking' as a warning. Some birds, whose territories are not being invaded, reply, and the air becomes full of a multitude of calls. The visitors are tolerated until morning, when they are hurried on their way with the sound of more 'chinking' ringing in their ears. This distinctive sound is heard less and less in the new year as more blackbirds sleep in their own territories, although some cock blackbirds continue the habit into the breeding season and 'chink' close to their nests containing eggs or young as dusk approaches.

The method of assembling a short distance from the communal roost is a feature of the behaviour of the pied wagtail. On winter afternoons, certain open spaces, such as school playing fields, front lawns in open-plan housing estates or the tarmac-covered areas around factories, become dotted with pied wagtails feeding on the ground, a sure sign that they have a communal roost a short distance away. As more arrive, some from several miles away, the birds begin to fly over and around the roost, perching on lamp-posts, fences, television aerials and rooftops, surveying the area to make sure that the coast is clear. As the light fades, they drop down, one after another, into the particular spot where they will spend the night. Their roosts are sometimes located in very busy places such as on city buildings or in a tree in a well-used street.

Apart from the starlings, few of the winter flocks of birds venture far into towns, day or night, unless it is a very severe winter. Many other birds, however, also indulge in communal roosting. These include greenfinches, goldfinches, siskins, redpolls, bullfinches, fieldfares, redwings, mistle thrushes, woodpigeons, rooks, magpies and crows. There are naturally variations in numbers and locations in each case.

The value of this phenomenon of communal roosting is probably three-fold: firstly, safety in numbers, in that a nocturnal predator has less chance of surprising several hundred sleeping birds than one or two; secondly, the sharing of knowledge about availability of food; and thirdly, the benefit of warmth. Long-tailed tits, for example, sleep side by side with their bodies

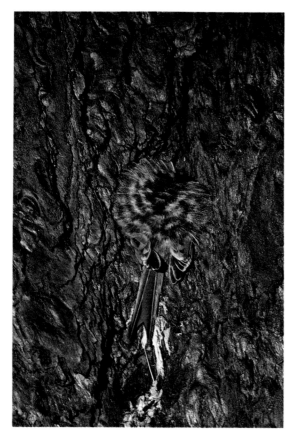

This photograph shows the typical roosting pose of the treecreeper. Note the marks of the droppings below the roosting spot.

pressed tightly together when the weather is cold.

The normal method of roosting employed by the treecreeper is unique among British birds. The bird snuggles into a hollow or light depression in the bark of a tree, fluffs out its feathers, tucks its beak under its front and sleeps in an upright position with its front pressed close to the tree and its tail giving support from below. The cryptic colouring of the back feathers provides camouflage and the bark of the tree gives shelter. Some of these hollows are natural depressions in the trunk, but treecreepers sometimes use their beaks to pick away at the rotten wood of dead elms or pines, or the soft fibrous bark of the Wellingtonia, the treecreeper's favourite roosting tree. Treecreepers may sleep singly but, in areas where there are few trees with the right kind of bark, several individuals may converge from some distance to sleep on one tree. Treecreepers usually choose a spot near the base of the tree and leave tell-tale white droppings at the bottom of the little hollows in which they sleep, so their roosts are relatively easy to detect.

Before we finish with the habit of communal roosting, we should consider the wren, another bird which will sleep pressed close to its brethren on very cold nights. An old song thrush nest, house martins' nests and a coconut shell have been recorded as locations for communal wren roosts, as well as the interior of sheds and barns, but nest-boxes seem especially favoured. It was, in fact, inside a nest-box that forty-six wrens were once found sleeping, crammed together in layers, lying on each other's backs. There has been at least one instance of a small party of wrens sleeping together in a nest-box throughout the winter months, but as a rule they will sleep individually when the nights are less cold. A great variety of sites may then be used, the majority being holes and cavities such as woodpecker holes, spaces in and behind old bark, gaps in brickwork and under the roofs of buildings, behind loose planks on wooden sheds and in haystacks.

So far, we have observed a pattern of birds sleeping in ones and twos during the summer and roosting socially for some or all of the winter. The house sparrow has developed a different but very successful alternative. From mid-summer onwards, young house sparrows group themselves into small feeding parties which, in some areas, become large flocks which the adults join as they finish breeding. They may feed some distance from their nesting colonies and, around smaller towns where agricultural land is within easy reach, they spend the days at this time of the year in the fields, feeding on the grain as it ripens, and later on the grain spilt during harvesting. During these months they sleep around the fields in hedgerows and copses, although some of the adult birds fly back to their nest-holes each night. With the majority of species, the communal roosts break up at the end of winter as the birds move away to their breeding territories. Nevertheless, the large roosts of house sparrows last only until the food bonanza comes to an end, when they return to the comfort of their nest-holes for the cold winter nights that lie ahead.

The garden birds not mentioned thus far are mainly solitary in their bedtime habits. Dunnocks and robins sleep alone in hedges and shrubs somewhere within their territories, as do the British chaffinches, unlike their continental cousins in their communal roosts. Most of the tits, with the exception of the long-tailed, roost singly in tree-holes and other cavities (although coal tits, which often inhabit coniferous woodland where holes are sometimes at a premium, are known to sleep among the needles in pine trees). A few of the tits will sleep in and around the local gardens, but they are more likely to commute some distance between the gardens and the trees in the local park, copse or woodland. There, tits and nuthatches sleep in natural holes and cracks in the trunks, in the space behind bark, or in old woodpecker holes. As for the woodpeckers themselves, they roost in holes carved out by others of their kind in previous years. It is claimed that woodpeckers also carve out holes especially for roosting but this appears to be, at most, an infrequent occurrence outside the breeding season. If no suitable hole is available, a woodpecker will sleep, head tucked in behind, lying along a sturdy branch at about a 45° angle.

Finally, there are two interesting variations of roosting which merit a brief mention, both associated with the cold winters of northern countries. Firstly, house sparrows sometimes build nests in small holes to be used solely as roosts rather than for breeding purposes. Secondly and remarkably, two species at least, the redpoll and willow tit, are known to tunnel into the snow to sleep.

Spring and Summer

During the spring and summer, most of the garden birds change their roosting habits, for, during the breeding season, the birds' movements are restricted by the presence of a nest and the need to defend territories. At the same time, they have a greater choice of roost sites, because on warm nights it is not so necessary to find a sheltered spot, and the abundant foliage ensures seclusion from predators in many places where winter roosting would be out of the question.

With the onset of spring, birds get less and less sleep at night. This is only partly explained by the increase in day-length, for at this time of the year they become active and start singing earlier and earlier in relation to sunrise. In winter, the opening burst of song precedes sunrise by a short time only, but in April and May the same birds will commence singing as much as an hour and a half before sunrise. This is particularly so in the case of the thrushes.

As the male has the responsibility of guarding the territory, he is likely to be busy before his mate and, if eggs have already been laid, she will appear considerably later in the morning and settle down for the night long before he ends his day. Later, when the eggs hatch, driven on by the instinct to feed her young, she will suddenly have a far longer day, leaving the nest before sunrise instead of after and continuing to forage for food until much later in the day, probably well after the sun has set. As the nestlings grow, both parent birds will gradually work even longer hours, although the cock usually goes to his roost before the hen joins her offspring in the nest.

When the nest has been built or when the first egg has been laid, the female of almost all the garden birds sleeps in it and continues to do so as long as there are eggs or unfeathered young there. In most cases, from the robin right up to the rooks and crows and birds of prey, the cock bird sleeps in the same bush or tree, or one close by, and keeps guard. Pairs of house sparrows, on the other hand, sleep together in the nest-hole and pairs of long-tailed tits also sleep together in their domed nest once it is complete. As they line the nest with anything up to 2,000 feathers, it provides truly luxurious accommodation.

Another variation is provided by the woodpeckers. The male has a stronger drive to nest than his mate and is much more energetic in carving out a nest-hole. Once it is large enough for him to do so, he will spend the night inside, and later it is he rather than the hen who incubates the eggs at night. Among some of the other species, such as blue tit and great tit, this responsibility is so exclusively the hen's that the young will die if anything happens to the female. For, although the male tit continues to feed the brood during the daylight hours, he does not sleep on them at night. Consequently they die from cold unless sufficiently mature to have grown a good covering of feathers.

A minority of adult females among the garden birds will continue to cover their nestlings right up until the time they fledge. The house sparrow is a case in point. Young birds are sufficiently well feathered, however, during their last few days in the nest, to keep themselves warm at night, so most females sleep elsewhere at this time.

When a parent bird sleeps in the nest, it does so lying prone on its belly, just like the nestlings do until they leave the nest. Then they adopt the 'adult' posture as described earlier.

For the swallow, swift and house martin, the nest is much more of a base and a shelter. Both male and female of all three species sleep together at the nest site from the time nesting begins until shortly before they leave on their return migration. They spend the night crouching or lying on their fronts in the nest, on the rim or on a flat ledge or beam adjacent to the nest or a foot or so away. On cold nights, they may edge towards each other and press close together to conserve heat. Pairs of swifts have even been observed sleeping on top of one another for added warmth.

When the young swifts leave the nest, they are unlikely to return there that summer. Young swallows and house martins, by contrast, return to the nests, with their parents, for several nights after their fledging. The house martins squeeze themselves into the nest cup, although there are usually some old unused nests under the same eaves which can serve as a second dormitory. These are useful for the young birds to sleep in later, when the female requires her nest for her second or third clutch of eggs; although, by this time, the young of earlier broods are beginning to move away from the colony. Swallows sometimes also crowd together in and around the nest cup itself for the night but, as most swallow nests are inside sheds and buildings, there are likely to be several ledges, shelves and beams nearby upon which the individual birds can range themselves.

Finally, mention must be made of the roosting habits of these three birds when on migration. Swallows, and to a far lesser extent house martins, roost in reed beds, on occasions in vast numbers, just as they do in their winter quarters in southern Africa. By comparison, the night-time habits of migrating swifts, as described by David Lack in *Swifts in a Tower*, are varied and sometimes quite bizarre. The swifts' ability to sleep on the wing has already been noted, but in very bad weather parties of swifts may be forced down to seek shelter for the night. It is then that the swift reveals its extraordinary ability to cling onto a vertical surface (a tree or even a wall, for example) by means of its tiny, sharp claws; the tail is pressed inwards, in the manner of a woodpecker, to provide additional support. On occasions they will sleep clinging to a vertical surface, huddled together for warmth in great bundles, which can be a metre or so across and up to three metres in length. The birds in the middle are kept warm by the others, while those at the extremities may die from exposure. Yet by this method far more survive than would do so otherwise. They may even enter buildings to escape torrential rain or a snowstorm in the winter months.

CHAPTER 2

COURTSHIP
AND NESTING

It is very difficult to define the exact point at which a bird's breeding cycle commences. Does a male robin begin the breeding process when it sings for the first time, when it establishes a territory or when it forms a pair with a female? Alternatively, should we go back even further to the post-juvenile moult when the bird assumed its adult plumage? One place to begin is with the birds' sexual development.

Long before the conventional signs of spring appear, the sexual development of most of the resident birds has begun, triggered off initially by the increase in day-length. The sexual organs continue to develop as the temperatures rise and, in exceptionally mild winters, a few birds raise young as early as February. Even in a normal winter, several events that are preparatory to breeding in the spring have occurred before Christmas and many of the garden residents have formed pairs, claimed territory and started singing by January or February. By late February or early March, even in wintry conditions, a few mistle thrushes and tawny owls may have begun laying, magpies and rooks are nest-building and the search for a nest-site is under way among most of the other resident species.

There are, however, often considerable variations in birds' behaviour. The breeding cycle in the south of Britain can be as much as a month ahead of events in the far north.

TERRITORY

For many of the garden birds, a territory is an area in which two birds pair, mate, nest and raise their young, and which is defended (by means of display, fighting and possibly song) from other adults of the same species; it may also, in fewer cases, provide enough food for the two birds and their young. However, there are many variations on this theme.

Firstly, there is the matter of the size of a territory. At one extreme, there are birds which nest colonially and defend just the small space around the nest: house martin, house sparrow, jackdaw and rook, for example. The swift defends only the interior of the nest-hole itself. Other species nest together in less tightly-knit colonies: there may

be two or three swallows' nests in one barn or shed, probably separated by a few metres, and in one tree or small clump of trees there can be three or four goldfinch or greenfinch nests. Similarly, pied flycatchers defend only that part of their territory immediately around the nest-hole and the different holes are sometimes only a few metres apart. Nevertheless all of these birds will fight fiercely if a neighbour approaches too closely, no matter how small the territory might be.

Although they do not nest communally, long-tailed tits and woodpigeons also occasionally build their nests with as little as a dozen metres between them, if there is a shortage of good nest-sites. Long-tailed tits are usually on fairly good terms with their neighbours and will even allow other adults, which have failed to breed success-fully, to assist in the feeding of the young in the nest. This may be partly explained by the fact that many species show far greater territorial aggression in the early stages of breeding, usually until the eggs hatch. Once young are in the nest, even some of the most territorial of species will tolerate trespassers.

At the other extreme from the colonial nesters, there are birds including crow, mistle thrush and the woodpeckers which have territories extending sometimes to many hectares. If a population increases, however, territories of all birds can be compressed, but only up to a point, beyond which there will be too much disturbance and breeding will not take place. In different circumstances, territories can expand. After the severe British winter of 1962–3, the populations of many birds had dwindled drastically; consequently, some territories were extremely large. In such circum-stances, however, the larger area is not likely to be so jealously guarded if another bird lays claim to it.

So the size of territory is infinitely variable, depending on the local population density of the species concerned, the stage reached in the nest-ing programme, as well as the size, shape and suitability of the available habitat. In his study of the robin, David Lack considered 0.6 hectare ($1\frac{1}{2}$ acres) the 'norm', whereas David Snow found 0.2 hectare ($\frac{1}{2}$ acre) to be the average territory size for garden blackbirds. This last figure might seem rather small but most of the garden dwellers can manage with that size or even, at a pinch, 0.15 hectare ($\frac{1}{3}$ acre). These include tits, dunnock, willow warbler, blackcap and even the robin, as well as the colonial nesting birds already mentioned. In fact, only a few small birds, such as wren, marsh tit and chaffinch, generally appear to have territories much larger than this in gardens and suburbs. The garden birds are nothing if not adaptable and, because good breeding habitat is at a premium in most parks and gardens, they often nest there successfully in far smaller territories than they would expect to have in woodland or open country. Even mistle

House martins, and to a slightly lesser degree swallows, nest very close to others of their own kind, defending only a small area around their nests. Here, however, swallows have nested alongside house martins. Two young swallow nestlings beg for food from a parent house martin which is feeding its own chicks in the nest.

thrush territories can be smaller than 0.8 hectare (2 acres) and magpies' nests can be less than 100 metres apart.

The function of territory is still not clear in all cases. It is generally agreed, though, that its value lies in spacing out different breeding pairs, enabling them to pair, court, mate and nest in relative peace without too much competition and disturbance from others of their kind. Furthermore, among species that do not nest colonially, it ensures a fair share of the available food supply, so that parents with a brood of hungry youngsters do not waste time searching for food in a place which has just been cleared by another pair.

Nevertheless, even very territorial birds like robin, blackbird and wren will sneak silently into an adjacent territory in search of food or water, particularly if the owners are feeding young, when territorial defence is at a low ebb. Where the colonial nesting birds are concerned, clearly, sufficient food is not going to be found within a 'territory' of a few square metres.

Some birds (jackdaw and rook, for instance) are extremely gregarious at all times of the year; when we look at other birds, however, we can see that the habit of nesting close together may have come about as a result of specialised feeding methods. Flying insects and seeds constitute two shifting and unpredictable food supplies. A bird relying heavily on either of these would gain no advantage by claiming a territory within which it had found an abundance of food. Flying insects swarm in different places as the weather changes and summer progresses, while seeds are plentiful in different areas as various plants produce seeds. So a plentiful supply of food can disappear totally while another becomes available a mile or so away.

Swifts, swallows and house martins, therefore, leave their tiny defended 'territories' to catch aerial insects elsewhere and carry them back to their young in their gullets. Likewise all the finches, with the exception of the chaffinch and brambling, feed their young on a diet which consists largely or wholly of seeds. They, too, carry the food in their gullets, which permits relatively large quantities to be collected, so the number of journeys between nest-site and feeding-grounds is reduced. Dependent as they are on an erratic supply of food, these birds possibly enjoy the advantage of being able to pool information. It is not unusual at such communal nest-sites to see the parent birds all flying off in the same direction to forage for food.

The finches that use this method have another adaptation to cope with the variable nature of the seed crops. If they are to raise a second brood, as is usually the case, the second nest, and therefore a different territory, is often established some distance away in a completely new area. A pair of greenfinches or goldfinches which start to nest in a garden in mid-summer have almost certainly made an earlier attempt at breeding elsewhere.

Quite apart from this and among other species as well, territorial borders are not always permanently fixed over a period of time, although a prominent feature such as a wide open space or a woodland edge may conveniently define part of a boundary for many years and a number of different owners. Often, as territory-owners die,

or the territory changes hands for some other reason, the boundaries shift slightly. Surviving adults of most species do inhabit roughly the same area from one season to the next and many occupy the same territory, but if an adjacent territory falls vacant, a male will often annex it and, if it is a more desirable residence, claim it for his own.

Mention has already been made of the tendency among some birds to trespass repeatedly on another's territory. If the owner recognises the intruder as a neighbour, he will normally drive him away immediately. Sometimes, however, strangers are allowed to pass through undisturbed as long as they show no aggression. In fact, trespassing birds usually remain quiet and submissive and, as a result, among some species where the sexes are alike, a male might be taken for a female and treated accordingly.

Apart from the swift, which does not breed until it is nearly two, most small and medium-sized birds are able to breed in their first year. Some of the larger birds, such as crows, do not breed until later years and, where intruders are tolerated by a breeding pair, it is likely that the individuals concerned are young, non-breeding birds, probably from a previous year's brood.

Females are generally less aggressive than their mates and leave most of the territorial defensive duties to them, for at least part of the nesting period. Nevertheless, at particular times, the hens of certain species drive off uninvited guests: female blackbirds, for example, can often be seen chasing other blackbirds of either sex in the spring. In other situations, the female will help the male to drive off other birds in what can sometimes be a lively skirmish. A pair of magpies joining forces to launch a two-pronged attack at other magpies entering their territory can present the human observer with an exciting and dramatic spectacle. Although it is not a hard and fast rule, territory holders are usually the victors in any dispute over their territory.

The form of defence varies from species to species. A robin flies straight towards a rival and, while perching possibly only half a metre or so away, alternately sings and thrusts the red breast feathers forward. If this visual and oral warning does not have the desired effect, the owner of the territory will physically set upon the enemy. A cock blackbird, however, does not sing in threat but bounces silently towards the rival; the neck is stretched, the beak pointed upwards and wings and tail are lowered. If the rival cock does not take the hint, a fight will ensue. The two birds claw and peck at each other as they flutter vertically upwards. When they return to the ground, they square up to each other once more, crouching with tails fanned and beaks agape. Male woodpigeons oppose one another on a branch nodding curiously and flicking their wings. As the two combatants approach each other, the wings are used to slap the opponent, the intention being to dislodge him from the perch.

A commonly used aggressive tactic is the so-called 'supplanting attack' whereby the attacker flies at an adversary and chases it from its perch, alighting there a second or two after the other bird has vacated it. If the intruder does not leave the territory after repeated warnings, the owner will start to fight.

However, actual physical combat is unlikely to occur between established neighbours. A balance of power exists between them and it is to both their advantages to avoid continually coming to blows. Instead, by singing and posturing at the mutually agreed border that divides their territories, the two sensibly avoid the need to fight.

Territories are also held outside the breeding season by some birds. The robin is unusual in that, when breeding has finished, in June or July, the pairs break up and those females that do not migrate take up territories of their own. After the moult, they sing, threaten and, if necessary, fight in the defence of their territory, possibly coming into conflict with former or future mates who may hold adjoining territories. Those that are defended at this time of year are considerably smaller than those held by a pair in the spring. This situation continues until December, January or February when a male, now singing with greater intensity, attracts a female to join him in his territory. She now ceases to show any aggression and leaves all territorial defence to him until nest-building commences in March or April when they defend the territory together.

No other British garden bird has an arrangement quite like this, although a few females, including some song thrushes and blackbirds, hold small temporary territories for a time during the winter. In Britain, however, many of the mature garden birds remain on their territories throughout the autumn and winter months and defend it or part of it for some of this time (blackbird, wren, dunnock, chaffinch, magpie, crow, starling, house sparrow, woodpecker and nuthatch, for example). In very cold conditions virtually no territorial behaviour occurs as the birds channel all their energies into trying simply to stay alive.

In autumn, some of the territorial activity is caused by the usual brief recurrence of sexual behaviour which shows itself in a sudden upsurge in singing, chasing and occasional attempts at breeding. Later, this dies down until December or the new year when the areas to be used for breeding are mapped out once more. Young birds which have possibly been allowed to hold parts of the adults' territories are driven out to search for a place of their own.

So important is possession of a territory that most garden birds are unable to breed without one; furthermore, with the exception of those species which can pair in a flock, before acquiring a territory, a male without a suitable area cannot hope, in normal circumstances, to gain a mate. Undoubtedly there are many young birds which, though capable of breeding, fail to do so for this reason. Among the common species, this is most likely in areas where there is a great deal of competition for available habitat and nest-sites. If territory-owning tits, robins or blackbirds, for example, are removed, their places are taken, sometimes in a matter of minutes, by others. These new arrivals are either from this 'floating' population, or they may be birds, again probably first-year birds, which have had to make do with an inferior territory.

SONG

Bird song is often explained as a means whereby a territory-holding male attracts a female and warns off prospective rivals. This is partly or wholly true for several garden birds, yet there are exceptions to this rule—some of them quite inexplicable.

Certainly, for some like robin, wren, blackcap, chiffchaff and willow warbler, the song is very much bound up with aggression; rival males will sing at each other as a warning and to proclaim ownership of the territory. Indeed, in the case of some of these birds, where the two sexes are virtually identical, song may be an important factor in identifying male from female, in other words, enemy from prospective mate. A recording of the appropriate song will elicit aggressive behaviour and an answering song from some of these species, although for the robin the visual stimulus of the red breast feathers is far more powerful. The most violent reaction towards such a recording comes from the willow warbler and chiffchaff and it seems likely that, for two birds so alike, a more than usual importance is attached to song in distinguishing between the two species.

There are some puzzling anomalies in the role of song in pair formation. The peak of song for most of the resident birds comes in April, May and June, long after the majority of them have formed pairs. Some, such as blackbirds, do not sing at all until the breeding cycle is well advanced, and often the richest and most beautiful song performances are given when the hen is incubating the eggs. Possibly, this aspect of early song is more important for the summer visitors: the males of many species establish a territory as soon as they arrive and are in full song when the females appear in search of a mate a few days later.

Another puzzle is the use of the 'sub song', a quiet, subdued variation, often very different from the full song. It is sometimes only audible at close range, almost as if the bird is indulging in a private practice session. There is also communal singing, which starlings and house sparrows, among others, take part in, even in mid-winter, when neither sexual nor aggressive instincts seem to be involved.

Even more curious, perhaps, is the purpose of mimicry. Jay, jackdaw, blackcap, chaffinch, redstart, song thrush and starling are just some of the birds which can copy sounds, not just of other birds, but also of mammals, including human whistles, and machinery. The imitation can be extraordinarily effective and quite experienced birdwatchers can be fooled. The starling is particularly skilful, in this respect; many of them can give an excellent rendition of the green woodpecker's 'yaffle'. One explanation for mimicry is that, in some species, a male may more easily attract females if he possesses a richly varied song, so the addition to his repertoire of alien, mimicked sounds may be to his advantage.

It is certainly true that bird song is subject to considerable regional and national variations which even the human ear can easily detect. We also know that there are many features of bird sounds that the human ear cannot pick up but which, presumably, the birds themselves can distinguish. Neighbouring birds can recognise each other's songs and they notice when a new bird's song is introduced. Among some species, especially those like greenfinch and goldfinch which breed close together, song variations between individuals are important in identifying different males.

It is worth noting, at this point, that not all garden birds possess a song: the long-tailed tit does not, nor do the corvids, although the rook makes an attempt at singing. There are some species which use calls in the way other birds use song, for self-advertisement and to indicate ownership of territory. Magpies proclaim possession of territory by giving their rattling calls and raising their tails while perched prominently on a tall tree near the nest-site. The green woodpecker's laughing call is heard most frequently in the breeding season and the greater and lesser spotted woodpeckers 'sing' by drumming on dead timber. Just as song birds have favourite song

Song is important for many territorial birds: most commonly it is used by the male to advertise possession of his territory, to warn off other males and, possibly, attract a female. In spring and early summer, the lovely song of the willow warbler (above) is an ever-present sound in woods, parks and large gardens. The robin's song may be heard at almost every time of the year.

perches around their territories, so these two woodpeckers have regular drumming posts in different parts of theirs, from which they give a short, rapid rattle of notes to proclaim ownership of territory. The piece of wood chosen will be hard, resilient and possibly hollow so that the sound can sometimes carry up to nearly a kilometre. Occasionally, pieces of metal, such as plates on telegraph poles, are used to create a particularly powerful effect. Both sexes drum, just as female song birds sometimes sing.

Between February and the end of the breeding season, the dunnock sings its sweet, tinkling warble, but from autumn through to January this normally quiet and unobtrusive little bird proclaims its presence and defies rivals with a loud and piercing 'tseep' call, usually uttered from a prominent perch on the top of a bush or fence.

There is an interesting correlation between song and the colour of a bird's plumage. The most impressive songsters, blackbird, song thrush, mistle thrush, wren, dunnock, robin, blackcap, garden warbler, willow warbler and, of course, the nightingale, have dull or muted colours. Clearly, sartorial brilliance is of little value to birds which inhabit, or originally inhabited, thick vegetation or woodland. By contrast, some of the most colourful songbirds, like bullfinch and redstart, have thin, weak, rather disappointing songs compared to many of their close relatives, and the most dazzling of all British birds, the kingfisher, although reputed to possess a song, puts it to use (if indeed it has one at all) so rarely that it is hardly ever heard.

Remarkably, apart from a few bitterly cold days in winter, there are few days in the year when one cannot hear at least one bird singing. The quietest time is not during the grey days of winter but in mid-summer, even though some garden birds may still be breeding at that time. This is the time when most birds are undergoing their moult, or are about to begin doing so, and birds do not sing while moulting. During the latter part of June and much of July, the parks and gardens are silent, except for sporadic bursts of song from wrens, woodpigeons and possibly one or two other species.

By the end of July or early August, the young robins from early broods attempt their first notes, and in the middle of August robins are singing everywhere as more and more adults complete their moult. From then until December, robins are the only birds to sing consistently, and even their song is a pale version of the full-blooded spring version. There are, however, also intermittent, desultory attempts from a few other birds—willow warblers and chiffchaffs as they wend their way southwards, the familiar mixture of chuckles, clicks and whistles from a starling or the occasional rush of notes from a wren.

Curiously, it is in mid-winter, on mild days in December, that bird song begins once more to intensify and increase. The robin's song becomes fuller and richer, starlings sing more regularly and they are joined on occasions by song thrushes, goldcrests, great tits and coal tits. Mistle thrushes sing in December, too, but not just on bright, spring-like days. This bird's song can be heard on dark, rainy days: hence its nickname of 'stormcock'.

In early February some other birds, such as chaffinch, wren, dunnock and blackbird, begin to sing again, although it is not until the second half of March that they sing strongly and consistently. The blackbird often chooses to give its first performances of the year at dusk, sometimes in places where it could not possibly set up a territory. The glorious, rich notes of a blackbird song ringing out above the sound of traffic in a crowded town centre, well after lighting-up time on a February evening, is unforgettable.

By the end of February, or early March, the whistling song of the nuthatch may be heard and great spotted woodpeckers start drumming. Now that almost all the residents have announced their presence, the first song from the summer visitors is awaited. In the south, any time after mid-March, the first chiffchaff might be heard singing, announcing that millions of other migrants are following behind.

PAIRING, COURTSHIP AND MATING

The length of courtship varies from species to species. At one end of the scale are the summer visitors with little time to waste. A pair of willow warblers, blackcaps or redstarts, for example, may pair within minutes of meeting; copulation may take place and the nest-building may have begun within four or five days. At the other extreme, there are many resident birds which pair up in autumn or winter, months before they commence nesting.

The males of certain species are required to display and posture furiously in front of the female if they are to win her. In some cases, these displays recur later in the breeding season and, just before egg-laying and incubation begin, often precede and indeed stimulate copulation. On the other hand, there are some species among which the actual pair-formation is accompanied by little show of excitement. For instance, a female robin slips into a singing male's territory and, after a brief period of aggression from the male, she is accepted. From then until nest-building, the two birds largely ignore each other although they spend part of each day feeding quite close together. Where blackbirds are concerned, the pairing may not even be accompanied by song for, as we have seen, many cock blackbirds do not sing in earnest until late March, by which time the majority of pairs have been established.

In most winters, pairs of any of the resident species can be formed before the turn of the year. Among the more gregarious birds, such as finches, pairs are established within the winter flocks, and in a mixed tit feeding party there are likely to be some birds which have already paired. Sometimes, by careful observation, it is possible to pick these birds out as males squabble together guarding their chosen hens from ardent admirers. Even the long-tailed tit, the most sociable of all the garden birds, becomes slightly tetchy and quarrelsome as the flock starts to break up into pairs in February or March.

By and large, the most excited and intense displays are seen as the breeding season approaches. In his sexual display, the male house sparrow raises and fans his tail feathers, lowers his wings and pushes out his chest. Consequently, his black bib, creamy wing bars and grey back and rump are conspicuous. The cock blackbird's sexual posturing involves the male in lowering and fan-

ning his tail, sleeking his neck feathers and raising his rump feathers.

A female, during these sexual skirmishes, will have her own set of signals to reply to the male's. During pairing, she will indicate whether she has accepted the male's advances. Later, when mating is to take place, she may initiate copulation herself. The hen house sparrow will lower and flatten her whole body, partly open her wings and vibrate them rapidly in the 'invitation position'. The female wren squats down in a similar way, spreads her wings slightly and fans her quivering tail. The male, if he is receptive, will recognise the signals, raise his tail, move it from side to side and then mount her.

In a number of species, the hen bird, shortly before and perhaps during incubation, will flutter her wings like a young bird begging for food. The message this time is that she wants her mate to feed her. The female robin calls persistently and intensely with a single-note, piping sound and receives the proffered food with excited wing-quivering, just as her fledglings will do in four or

During 'courtship feeding', the hen usually begs for food from her mate just as young birds do from their parents. For some species, such as bullfinches, this behaviour probably serves to strengthen the bond between the two birds.

five weeks' time. Coition sometimes follows shortly afterwards. The accepted term for this behaviour is 'courtship feeding'. This is slightly misleading, because in most cases it takes place long after the female has been courted, and won, by the male. Even among summer visitors, it occurs several days after the pair has been formed. Possibly 'nuptial feeding' would be a more appropriate description.

Robin, blue tit, great tit, treecreeper, nuthatch, flycatchers, kingfisher, corvids, gulls and most finches (the chaffinch is the major exception) all indulge in nuptial feeding. Although for a few species this behaviour seems to be little more than a formalised ritual, for others it is of considerable value, providing the female with additional nourishment at a time when she is forming the eggs. If the hen is to carry out all the incubation, nuptial feeding may also serve as a prelude to the important matter of the cock feeding her while she is on the eggs.

There is a tremendous range of sexual display employed by garden birds. Some displays, like the robin's, are elementary and undistinguished; others are more conspicuous; a few are complex and highly ritualised. For many species, display is a decidedly one-sided affair with the male doing his utmost to impress the female while she studiously ignores him or flies away. Either of these courses of action may be a prelude to the hen's acceptance of the male: although she appears uninterested in his advances, she most certainly is taking note of them and may suddenly present herself for copulation; so, too, her flying away may be an invitation for him to chase her.

Furious and excited chases are a feature of bird behaviour in spring. The male dunnock, in hot pursuit of his mate, flits and hops through the vegetation or along the ground rapidly flicking his wings upwards and raising and lowering his tail. The male goldcrest does the same among the branches of a tree, his wings lowered and quivering, his yellow crest feathers raised to show the orange-gold feathers in the centre. Very similar chases take place with the chiffchaffs and willow warblers, accompanied by much wing-flicking and puffing out of body feathers; a male chiffchaff, when excited, will also bob up and down

and raise his tail like a wren. Great spotted woodpeckers chase each other around the tree trunks, emitting high-pitched, chittering calls.

These chases, which are indulged in by several other species, are sometimes caused by the cock's advanced sexual state—males invariably come into breeding condition days, or even weeks, before the females. The female's attempts at escape, however, are often very obviously half-hearted; if she really wanted to avoid the male's advances, she could easily do so by leaving his territory altogether. In fact, the chase may be initiated by the female herself by flying close to him enticingly.

Nevertheless, situations do arise when the female seems genuinely to want to escape, in particular if pursued by several males. Attempted mass 'rape' sometimes occurs, often when one male's intense display or copulation arouses the other male birds nearby. This phenomenon seems most common among the more numerous species (house sparrow and blackbird, particularly) and may well be partly caused by overcrowding, and the resulting shortage of breeding territories and nest-sites. Among these potential 'rapists', there are males which have been unable to secure a territory, and therefore a mate, and whose sexual instincts are being thwarted. The whole affair rarely lasts for more than a few seconds and the female is unlikely either to be actually raped or hurt. She is obviously cowed and intimidated, though, and may remain for some time, as if dazed, in the spot where she was cornered.

There is a very fine line between aggression and sexual display. When a female enters an unpaired male's territory for the first time, she will usually be threatened; her submissive behaviour reduces his hostility. Even when the two have accepted each other, however, there are features of their relationship, such as the chases described and some males' sexual postures, which look remarkably like aggressive behaviour.

Not all displays are either one-sided or apparently aggressive. There are several species which, after the initial forming of the pair, indulge in various mutual displays with characteristics resembling what a human understands by affection. 'Billing and cooing', an expression normally applied to affectionate human lovers, is a clear indication of the amorous reputations that pigeons and doves have had for hundreds of years. A male woodpigeon bows and fans his tail before the female and, as their passion increases, each nibbles the other's head, neck and bill. Pairs of rooks, crows, jackdaws and magpies also caress each other's beaks and appear to derive pleasure from mutual preening around the head and neck. Some tame corvids enjoy having their necks fondled just as much as a pet dog or cat. Other birds which show 'affectionate' behaviour towards each other, such as mutual preening and bill fondling, include swifts, goldfinches and greenfinches. Colonial-nesting birds have a greater tendency to join in elaborate and mutual rituals than birds which spend the breeding season isolated from others of their kind in large territories. The close proximity of other adults in breeding condition means that temptation, so to speak, is never far away. These activities, therefore, have an important role in strengthening the bond between the two birds.

Among some of these birds, communal displays take place. Up to half a dozen goldfinches may be seen fluttering in a group aerial display over the colony. On still, balmy evenings, screaming parties of swifts race around the buildings in the locality of their nest-colony. It is possible that these displays serve not only for self-advertisement of the individuals but also to strengthen the ties within the colony and to serve as a kind of group territorial display.

During the breeding season, a pair of bullfinches are extremely discreet and unobtrusive. They are virtually silent, there is no territorial display and no apparent aggression is shown; they simply get on with the job of nesting. However, the bond between them is very firm and this is strengthened by complex and elaborate ceremonies, the most notable being the mutual presentation, amid great excitement, of small twigs and other nesting material.

A very important kind of display, usually described as 'nest-invitation' or 'nest-calling', can be observed easily by anyone with a tit-box in the garden. From December onwards, blue tits begin inspecting prospective nest-holes: the male enters the hole over and over again, frequently poking his head out through the entrance-hole, urging the hen to examine the site. If she rejects it, the procedure is repeated at another hole in the territory; but even if she finds it suitable they go through the same performance many times in the weeks that follow and a final decision is not made until she starts to construct the nest inside, usually in April. In the intervening weeks, the birds spend part of each day feeding, resting, preening and possibly displaying within a few yards of the hole.

Other hole-nesting birds, such as the starling, take part in similar activities. The male pied flycatcher hangs on the outside of the hole or nestbox he has chosen and shows off his white wing bars to the female and may sing while clinging there. A cock redstart whirls in and out of the hole, repeatedly poking his head out from inside to show off the dazzling white patch on his forehead. The male wren, having built a selection of nests, tries to interest a hen in one of them by displaying and calling furiously near the entrance and flying inside.

A few birds which use open nests also have a 'nest-calling' display: the male selects a likely branch or fork and indicates as much to his mate. However, whether the male introduces the hen to a site of his choice or, as is more often the case, she searches for somewhere herself, the eventual outcome is the same: just as she decided whether or not the displaying male was acceptable at the start, so it is she who makes the final choice about where the nest is to be.

Once a brood of youngsters has been safely raised, there is no need for the two adult birds to share their lives together. That is not to say that some birds do not have lengthy, or even life-long, relationships. When considering small birds, however, such as the majority of garden birds, we must bear in mind that as many as one third or even half of the adults that breed one year may have died by the time the next spring arrives. In a very cold winter, the mortality is likely to be even higher. Therefore, a large number of the breeding population *have* to find a new partner.

For most small birds, a new breeding season represents a fresh start; previous relationships are usually forgotten and largely irrelevant. If two birds mate in successive years, it is more likely to be as a result of an affinity towards the territory or nest-hole than loyalty towards the partner. Nuthatches, marsh tits, woodpeckers and blackbirds are some of the garden birds which regularly remain paired for consecutive years and, probably in many cases, for life. All are very sedentary birds with a strong inclination to remain within one small area for the whole year. Compared with some other species, there is relatively little inter-change of personnel so, when the time for pairing comes round again, there is a strong likelihood that, if both have survived, the same two birds join up again. By contrast, the robin, for example, has a fairly fluid female population with the hens moving into a territory of their own in autumn or migrating. A hen robin may return to the territory of her former mate for the next breeding season but she is just as likely to be attracted by a singing male somewhere else, possibly her previous mate's next-door neighbour.

Among the true migrants, a repeat pairing is even less likely. Most summer visitors return to roughly the area where they spent the previous summer. The male arrives first, establishes territory and sings strongly until the females arrive. If the first female to appear accepts his advances, the pair is formed. Clearly it would be unwise for the cock to ignore all willing females in the hope that his former mate might turn up. They have not been together during the winter so he has no way of knowing if she has survived; if she does arrive, she may well join another male nearby.

In fact, very few small birds, even those that are residents, spend the winter months together as a pair. They may feed together in the same area, perhaps in the same flock, but probably pay no attention to each other for most of the autumn and winter period. So, even if they join together again in late winter or spring, they cannot be said to be permanently paired. On the other hand, a pair of house sparrows usually stay close together, from one breeding season to the next, enjoying the convenience and comfort of a shared nest-hole. The bullfinch is a special case. Although it cannot be stated categorically that all bull-

finches pair for life, the signs are that many pairs retain a strong sexual bond, not only during the breeding season, but throughout the rest of the year as well. Pairing for life is more common among larger birds: swans, certain birds of prey, and, of the garden birds, magpies, jackdaws and rooks. Some of these, particularly the corvids, stay close together, throughout the year.

Although the garden birds which remain 'faithful' to a partner over the years are in the minority, at least we can say that the majority are monogamous during a single breeding season. Yet, bigamy occurs occasionally in most species, including robin, blackbird and starling, and cases of polygamy may sometimes exist. There are a few species which make a habit of it, however: male dunnocks often have more than one hen, as do swallows, spotted flycatchers and many mature pied flycatchers. The most promiscuous of all, though, is the cock wren who usually has two or three females while the first broods are being raised and may replace them with other hens for later broods.

Bigamy and polygamy are more likely to arise among species in which the incubation is carried out entirely or largely by the hen. If the male takes a large share of this duty (as in the case of house sparrow, swift, kingfisher and the woodpeckers) his energies are fully directed towards the one nest. Instances of bigamy often occur when a new female arrives in the territory while the first female is incubating. Later, the cock bird helps his first mate feed her brood while the second clutch is being incubated. Should the two broods require feeding simultaneously, there is still no problem for, in most cases, the female can provide sufficient food on her own.

BUILDINGS AS NEST-SITES

Modern man has had a massive impact on the landscape in Britain, as in most other parts of the world, and vast numbers of creatures, including many species of birds, have suffered as a result. Intensive farming, industrial development, the spread of housing and road networks, and the accompanying disappearance of trees, hedgerows, marshes and heaths, pollution of land, river, sea and air, and countless other factors have contributed to the demise of so much wildlife. The birds of towns and gardens are the ones which have been able to tolerate, so far at least, man's destruction of and intrusion into their natural habitats, although only time will tell whether they can outlive any further desecration of the natural world.

In spite of this, the activities of man the builder have been to the distinct advantage of a few species. Many buildings, for example, offer nest-sites to cliff-nesting birds. The feral pigeons that are found in all towns and cities are descended from the cliff-dwelling rock dove and they have found, as has the kestrel, that high-rise buildings with ledges and projections of various kinds are a satisfactory substitute for a natural cliff. So, too, during the last quarter of a century or so, various species of sea birds, including fulmars, kittiwakes and herring gulls, have taken to nesting on roof-tops of buildings in seaside towns and even, in some cases, well inland on riverside warehouses and factories.

An obvious example around our homes is the house martin, whose ancestors built their nests under overhanging rocks on cliff faces as a few of the species still do today. Because there are far more houses with eaves than cliffs with convenient ledges, these birds have benefited from man's unintentional provision of nest-sites. The house martin's nest is an inverted mud igloo, the separate 'bricks' being balls of mud or clay which are carried in the beak and glued together with saliva onto the wall under the eaves of a house. When finished, the tiny entrance hole is just big enough for the parent birds to squeeze through; the inside is lined with straw, grass and feathers, onto which the eggs are laid. Many nests survive for years, but some collapse with a brood of young birds inside and these inevitably perish.

Swallows, on the other hand, actually enter a building to build their nest, a shallow open bowl made of mud strengthened with straw and lined with feathers. Unlike the house martin, the swallow does not build its nest beneath a projection but places it on a beam or ledge, or even uses a small object such as a fuse box or light switch for support. If no such site is available, the nest will be glued with mud and saliva to the side of a rafter, sometimes completely unsupported, which can prove a rather precarious arrangement, and such nests commonly collapse. Garden sheds, garages, outhouses, barns, dairies and similar buildings provide the swallow with nesting facilities as long as the birds can fly in and out freely. Only a small gap is needed (a broken pane of glass or an ill-fitting door, for example)—but once the entrance is blocked the eggs must be left to chill or the young to starve. Before man arrived on the scene, swallows must have had a limited choice, under rocks or the roofs of caves, and this species has now become almost wholly dependent for its breeding on what man has built. Yet there is now a danger that man may be taking away what he has given, for many buildings which once provided accommodation for swallows are gradually disappearing. On farms and in gardens, dilapidated timber sheds and ramshackle wooden garages are being pulled down to be replaced by neat brick or prefabricated buildings with their doors tightly shut against the swallow.

Many birds nest inside buildings but none so habitually as swallows. Shelves, beams and ledges are used in garden sheds, garages, barns and outbuildings of various kinds, usually in less built-up areas. These three youngsters are almost ready to leave the nest.

The swift is another species which relies on man's buildings for nest-sites. It habitually uses hollows and crevices under the roofs of older buildings in towns and cities. The nest, which is made on a flat surface, a ledge or rafter, is constructed of blades of grass, leaves, petals and other vegetation, caught in mid-air as they float on the wind and glued together with saliva. Like the swallow, after years of plenty, the swift too is finding its traditional nest-sites are falling victim to the demolition teams and being replaced by modern structures with no means of access.

There are many other garden birds which nest in and on buildings, although they are not so dependent on them as are the swift, swallow and house martin. Starlings and house sparrows frequently nest in holes in the fabric of a house, in wall-crevices, under roofs, in thatch, drainpipes or chimneys, anywhere in fact which provides shelter and space enough for the nest to be placed. The starling's nest, like the house sparrow's, will be an untidy conglomeration of straw, feathers and other bits and pieces. Both species are noisy as well and consequently often unwelcome as nesting birds. Although the house sparrow rarely nests far from human dwellings, the starling is a common nesting bird in woodland, usually using old woodpecker nest-holes in tree-trunks. Sometimes, though, a pair of starlings will wait until woodpeckers have excavated a new nest-hole and then evict the rightful owners.

Many of the garden birds are tree- or woodland-dwellers and the holes they find in buildings are acceptable alternatives to nest-holes in trees. Loose bricks, crumbling mortar and dislodged tiles will provide a tit with an entrance to a cavity

House sparrows are too large to enter a completed house martin's nest but they often nest in ones which are only partly built or in a poor state of repair. The house martins may return in spring to find house sparrows already occupying their nest of the previous year.

which may be large enough to use as a nest-chamber. Treecreepers have successfully reared young behind warped boards on a garden shed, an excellent substitute for the treecreeper's conventional woodland nest-site behind loose pieces of dead bark hanging from a tree trunk. Jackdaws, which use large holes in trees in woodland, regularly nest in chimney-pots on town buildings.

Another bird which sometimes nests in holes in man-made structures is the redstart. This is an unlikely occurrence in any area other than those country districts where redstarts are abundant, but, in such places, there have been many records of this species nesting in cavities in garden walls, outbuildings and even occupied dwellings and workshops. The spotted flycatcher is another summer visitor which is happy to live close to man. Nests are common on ledges and beams and in cavities in the brickwork of outhouses and sometimes occupied houses. The site chosen usually has the benefit of some cover or means of concealment, probably from a climbing plant or shrubs such as honeysuckle, but it can sometimes be surprisingly exposed and easy to find.

By contrast, a wren's nest is usually extremely well hidden. This species regularly nests around buildings, in crevices, under roofs, beneath loose tiles, behind crumbling brickwork, in drainpipes, in fact, in any cavity which offers sufficient space for the nest to be formed. Indeed, there seems no end to this bird's audacity and inventiveness. Edward Armstrong, in his study of the wren, lists some extraordinary nest-sites, including a wreath in a shed, a tramp's shirt left on a bush, a pair of trousers hung up to dry, the fold in a church curtain, animal carcasses and a human skull.

For those garden birds which do not nest in holes, a house and garden buildings can still supply many sites such as might be available in a woodland setting; the dark interiors of sheds and garages, which may approximate to the gloomier corners of a wood, offer a wealth of possibilities. Blackbirds, robins and, less commonly, song thrushes are willing to nest 'indoors' in sheds and garages. Nests have been placed on the seats of cars, beneath mudguards, and even under the bonnet. Old boots, bicycle saddle-bags, wheelbarrows, paint-tins and pockets in overalls, and even an unmade bed, are just a few other strange nest-sites. Usually all that is required for the open-cup nest is a support in the form of a shelf, beam or window ledge, the necessary seclusion being supplied by the exterior walls and roof of the building, ample protection from all wild predators, but not necessarily any defence against cats.

The pied wagtail can match any of the species already mentioned for outlandish nesting habits, sometimes displaying amazing audacity (or folly) in its choice of nest-site. Around factories and workshops, the cup-shaped nest, usually made of grasses, may be among piles of scrap-metal, stacks of building bricks or machinery. Near farms and around stables it may be placed amongst the straw. This species appears relatively unperturbed by human activity and apparently oblivious of noise. A pair which began nesting in the engine of an earth-mover, required for use, continued with their nesting when the nest, complete with a clutch of eggs, was carried to a similar position in an adjacent machine not in use. Another pair nested in a school playground, rearing several broods over a period of three years. Some of the nest-sites chosen were adjacent to the classroom walls.

NESTS IN NATURAL HOLES

We have already seen how some hole-nesting birds use holes in buildings as substitutes for natural cavities. However, many established suburban avenues, parks and gardens contain good numbers of mature trees providing many natural holes for these birds to use. Because many of the birds which visit and nest in gardens are really woodland-dwellers, an area of housing with a liberal scattering of mature trees represents the same opportunities as a wood with clearings.

The smallest tree-holes will be used by blue tit, coal tit, great tit and occasionally marsh tit. Inside the hole, the nest of a tit is made mainly of moss, with, in the case of the blue tit, some strands of grass and perhaps a few minute twigs. The hen wriggles her body in this to form a cup in which a warm, soft lining is placed. Blue tits and marsh tits usually use feathers as a lining, whereas coal tits and great tits favour hair or fur. However, as the lining may be made of almost any soft material, it is worth watching the tits during spring to see what they are collecting. If a dog has just been groomed, some of the hairs which have been brushed out may be used. Alternatively, the contents of the vacuum cleaner may be plundered if they have been emptied onto the rubbish heap. At least one pair of great tits had a nest with a bright purple lining, the hen having collected large quantities of carpet fluff which had passed through a vacuum cleaner.

A tits' nest can be completed in a day or two if the birds are in a particular hurry: they may have started their breeding late or be eager to make up for lost time if another nest elsewhere has come to grief. When desperately short of time, or if space is a problem, the foundation of the nest will be kept to a minimum. Occasionally, a female great tit may build a nest very quickly with a few strands of dead grass and virtually no moss at all.

Normally, though, the nest-building extends over a period of several days, up to a week or a little longer. If the weather takes a turn for the worse, the nest-building will be shelved until conditions improve.

For the tits, the size of the nest-hole is important. If it is over 28 mm in diameter, house sparrows can enter and usurp the site. Whereas this is not usually a problem some distance from human dwellings, where house sparrows are scarce or non-existent, in gardens it is an important consideration. An even bigger hole will permit a squirrel to enter and possibly take the eggs. In some areas, the tit population is so large that nest-holes are in short supply and bigger

Coal tits nest in all kinds of natural holes, as well as nest-boxes, but they especially favour holes among the roots of a tree. This one in a hole made by a small rodent at the base of a silver birch is typical.

holes may well be used, especially by the great tit which sometimes uses old woodpecker holes. The coal tit usually prefers a small hole, on or near the ground, frequently among the roots of a tree; even the holes of small rodents are taken over.

In some cases, tits will nest behind loose bark, but this is the classic choice of the treecreeper. To a tidy-minded gardener, dead bark hanging from a decaying tree might be an eyesore, but the temptation to remove it or, worse still, to fell the tree, should be resisted at all costs. Dead timber not only provides birds with a rich supply of food but the rotten timber may also persuade a pair of woodpeckers to chisel out a nest-chamber. Neither does it end there. Woodpeckers regularly return to use the same tree in subsequent years, usually making their nest-hole a little lower in the trunk than the previous year. In addition, because other species nest in old woodpecker holes, that one dead tree can provide excellent nesting accommodation for many birds of different species for years, until the tree falls down.

To some people whose gardens lack a 'wooded appearance' the thought of woodpeckers nesting near the house may seem incredible. Yet in those gardens with what estate agents romantically label a 'sylvan setting', this is not such a rare event. In one extreme example, a pair of great spotted woodpeckers were excavating a nest-hole in the back garden of a suburban house (where they had successfully reared a brood the previous year) at the same time as green wood-peckers were establishing themselves in a hole in a tree in the front garden. The green wood-peckers, as so often happens, were later ousted by a pair of starlings and nested in another garden nearby. The great spotted woodpeckers nested successfully.

The lesser spotted woodpecker, the rarest of the three woodpeckers, is also the least common in gardens, but there have been cases of it nesting quite close to houses. The nest-chamber is smaller, the entrance hole possibly as little as 32 mm across, and the situation high above the ground, in a rotten branch, as often as in the main trunk of a tree, so a nest of this species may easily go unnoticed.

Woodpecker nest-holes are invariably in old, decaying timber and never in healthy trees. Usually a new hole is excavated each spring but the green woodpecker, shown here, sometimes uses old nest-holes. This bird, a female, is in the process of regurgitating food for the nestlings inside the nest-chamber.

The great spotted, the most common of the three, almost invariably excavates itself a new nest-hole each year, a dead silver birch being the most favoured tree in many areas, whereas the green woodpecker is often willing to re-use a nest-hole from a previous year, after a brief spring-clean. When making a nest-hole, a wood-pecker attacks the tree fiercely, flicking wood-chippings left and right. On a still day, they drop to the ground at the base of the tree and are a useful clue to the existence of the nest; on a windy day, however, the evidence is blown far and wide.

The excavation continues usually for $1\frac{1}{2}$ or 2

weeks with the woodpecker gradually disappearing, head-first, into the hole, backing out at regular intervals with a beak full of chippings which are tossed away. Eventually, the bird can turn around inside and then it merely thrusts its head out of the hole and lets go of the debris. The tunnel is just large enough to permit entry, but it quickly opens out into a deep and wide chamber in which the eggs are laid on a bed of wood chippings. The arrival of a pair of starlings at this time might result in the woodpeckers being ousted and having to begin again elsewhere.

The tits have already been mentioned, but natural holes or those created in previous years by woodpeckers are also popular with other birds, such as redstarts, pied flycatchers and nuthatches. The nesting habits of the latter are unique among British birds. The nuthatch chooses a hole which is bigger than it requires. Then mud is packed around the inside of the existing hole until the entrance is just large enough for the bird to enter. When the mud dries, it hardens into a cement-like barricade against most predators. Finally, some dead leaves and possibly some small pieces of bark are carried into the hole and placed at the base of the nest-chamber as a cushion onto which the eggs will be laid.

Like the redstart, the pied flycatcher will only nest in wooded gardens and orchards in those few favoured areas of Britain where the species is quite common. It, too, uses dead leaves to form the nest but lines the cup with soft materials such as hair or grasses. The redstart's nest is slightly different in that the preferred entrance hole is usually considerably larger and the nest constructed mainly of grass and moss lined with feathers. The eggs of both the redstart and pied flycatcher are particularly beautiful, a clear bright blue.

NESTS IN VEGETATION

The majority of nests in an established garden will be open or cup-shaped, built in various hedges, bushes, shrubs and trees. Any overgrown, untended parts with long grass, weeds and thick brambles will usually prove especially attractive to a number of garden species.

The blackbird and song thrush, for example, are likely to place their large, deep bowls, built mainly of grasses and leaves, in any bush or hedge which can provide a degree of seclusion. Early in spring, before the leaves are out, evergreens are likely to be used. Sometimes the nest is merely placed on a firm, flat branch, but more often it is wedged in a fork between two or three branches. The mistle thrush's nest, on the other hand, is generally placed higher, frequently in a tall tree. The cup-nest may be laid on a sturdy lateral branch or wedged in a fork of the trunk like that of its two relatives, but often the site chosen is completely without leaf-cover so it is a regular victim of raids by magpies and jays.

The mistle thrush is not typical in this respect. Open cup nests are usually well hidden from view. A robin's nest can be in almost any situation but usually it is tucked out of sight in a small hollow in a bank or tree, among tangled roots or under a pile of leaves and other vegetation. There is sometimes a short tunnel entrance and the cup is formed out of dead leaves, grass and moss with a lining of hair. In spite of its eccentric nesting habits and its reputation for tameness, the robin is a shy bird when nesting and its nests are often difficult to locate.

The pied wagtail may also place its shallow cup-like nest amongst vegetation, almost always low to the ground. One was even placed on the soil in an ornamental flower tub hidden by the fronds of a miniature ground-creeping shrub.

One of the loveliest of nests belongs to one of the dullest of garden birds, the dunnock. It is almost always in a hedge or shrub, well-hidden but rarely far inside. Again, evergreens are popular, as they provide a good degree of screening, and thorn bushes are also used. The construction of the cup is neat and precise, grass and moss being woven together with a soft lining of fur or wool and one or two feathers upon which the eggs are laid. These are supremely beautiful, the colour of the sky on the finest summer's day.

The nest of the tiny goldcrest is charming too. The minute cup of moss and lichen is usually hung from the branches of a tall pine tree, but a garden ornamental conifer sometimes serves as an alternative. A nest may also be in ivy or honeysuckle tangles, but it is so tiny that it can be quite difficult to spot.

Another bird which makes an open nest is the blackcap, although in the breeding season it is almost exclusively a bird of woodland thickets rather than gardens. The nest is a lightweight hammock of loosely woven grasses skilfully slung from two or three small branches deep in the undergrowth, usually either in brambles or thick evergreen vegetation.

Finches' nests, which are common in gardens, are most often placed quite high up in trees and bushes rather than in low undergrowth. Any spreading tree with plentiful foliage may be used but cherry and other fruit trees, honeysuckle, hawthorn and conifers are especially favoured. All finches make open cup-shaped nests. The most appealing to the human observer are those of the chaffinch and goldfinch. Both are neat, beautifully moulded bowls made of moss, lichen and hair, tightly compacted together so that they look too small for the size of the birds. They look very much alike and may be built in similar situations, but the goldfinch's is more likely to be placed far out near the extremity of a branch and is often much higher. One goldfinch's nest, placed at the end of a very slim and supple branch in a roadside cherry tree, bounced up and down alarmingly each time a large vehicle swept by.

By comparison, the nests of the bullfinch and greenfinch can look quite sloppily put together. The greenfinch's, which is a loose cup made of woven grasses, small twigs, moss and other soft materials, is usually above head height in a bush or tree. Because the bullfinch's nest is comprised largely of twigs, it too looks extremely straggly compared to the beautifully neat, smooth-sided bowl of the chaffinch and goldfinch. Twigs which are too long may be used and jut out untidily. The eggs are laid in a cup lined with delicate shoots and hair. The nest is often extremely well hidden among dense foliage, and sometimes thorns, and it is less frequently lodged in a tree than the nests of the other finches just mentioned.

Looking rather like large versions of a bullfinch's nest, those of woodpigeon and collared dove are extremely rudimentary: a few twigs lumped together among the smaller branches of

A few species, such as the chiffchaff shown here, build domed or partly-domed nests. Often the nest is constructed from the vegetation in the immediate vicinity so it blends in well with its surroundings.

a tree, bush or tall hedge. These nests look almost flat, with apparently no rim to keep the two white eggs in place. In the case of the woodpigeon there is no lining on top of the twigs. Nests are usually at least three metres above the ground, with the collared dove particularly keen to nest high above the ground.

Of the birds so far discussed, none, except the wren, attempts to protect its nest by actually constructing a roof. Most garden birds are content to lay their eggs beneath a canopy already in existence, whether that be the roof of a shed, the eaves of a house, or the leaves of a tree or bush.

There are a few species, however, apart from the hole-nesters, that contrive to give their nests some protection from above. The hen robin, for example, sometimes places her open-cup nest just beneath some over-arching vegetation, such as grasses and dead leaves, in a bank or among the tangle of roots at the base of a mature tree, thereby creating a kind of curved roof above. Similarly, willow warblers and chiffchaffs construct domed or partly-domed nests, although

A long-tailed tit's nest is an amazing construction, a ball of moss, lichen and spider's silk, with a small side entrance and a lining of hundreds, sometimes thousands, of feathers. Although often well camouflaged, these nests are frequently predated, possibly because the adults are noisy and conspicuous around the nest.

the canopy often consists of some vegetation already *in situ* rather than materials brought by the bird from elsewhere. The nest of the willow warbler, in particular, is one of the most stunningly beautiful of all British birds, which no photograph can capture. The nest, which is cunningly concealed beneath grasses and tangled vegetation, is approached by a minute tunnel which leads down to a tiny cup lined with white or pale-coloured feathers.

In fact, few of the garden birds actually extend the sides of their nests upwards and close them in above with a roof made of materials that they have gathered. The only other ones that regularly go to so much trouble are the wrens, long-tailed tits, magpies and sparrows.

The wren's nesting habits around buildings have already been mentioned, but in such places it is not always possible to see the whole nest. To appreciate it fully, study one which is constructed in a thicket or bush; it is a complete ball, except for the entrance hole. It often blends in perfectly

with the surrounding vegetation because the outer skin usually contains many of the dead leaves, fronds (particularly bracken) and grasses amongst which it is sited.

Although not a common feature of gardens, the long-tailed tit's nest deserves special mention, for it is a miracle of skill and design. It is often found deep in a thicket of brambles, hawthorn, honeysuckle or gorse. The hundreds of pieces of moss and lichen which form the outer skin of the nest create a dappled appearance, permitting the nest to merge into the subtle pattern of shadows and light filtering through the branches of a thicket. Sometimes, though, there is little attempt at concealment and the nest may be simply lodged between the limbs of a tree, when the birds appear to rely wholly on the nest's natural camouflage. Unfortunately, a large proportion of these long-tailed tits' nests are raided and destroyed by predators. The outer shell of lichen and moss is woven and glued together with spider's silk and saliva; then feathers, sometimes in their thousands, are placed inside to make the interior warm and soft. When complete, this wonderful nest is little bigger than a tennis ball with a tiny side entrance just wide enough to permit a parent bird through, and so miraculous is its construction that the sphere expands as the young birds grow, while still being strong enough to hold a brood which can be in excess of ten. Not surprisingly, such a splendid creation takes considerable time to construct (up to three weeks with both birds sharing the work). The pieces of building material are collected, a little at a time, with the birds, on occasions, flying to and fro some considerable distance for them.

A magpie's nest is a massive edifice compared to the achievement of the long-tailed tit and the wren. It is an untidy large ball of broken twigs and mud, lined with fine roots and hair, with a side entrance. In open country, it may be built in a tall hedge, often amongst thorns, at the edge of a field, but in and around gardens it is more commonly placed near the top of a tall tree. The nest is clearly visible when it is being built in spring before the leaves are out, but it is well hidden two or three weeks later when the hedge or tree is in leaf. The huge construction is so

The cock wren builds several domed nests in his territory, one of which the female chooses and lines with feathers prior to egg-laying. Here, photographed over several days, a wren's nest can be seen taking shape.

sturdy that many survive for two years or more.

The house sparrow, as we have already seen, usually breeds in holes and niches of various kinds around buildings, so it is not possible to see the construction of the nest itself. However, this bird is related to the weavers, rather than the finches, so its instinct is to form a domed nest, which it will attempt to do even in a confined space, using grass, string, hair, paper and other oddments—some of which straggle out through the entrance hole. If space permits, this untidy ball can be about 30 cm across.

NEST-BUILDING

A consideration of the nest-building habits of the garden birds reveals some interesting variations.

For example, it is thought by many people that it is always the hen who builds the nest. Yet there are several garden bird species, including house sparrow, long-tailed tit, treecreeper, goldcrest, blackcap, woodpigeon, collared dove, swift, starling, jay, jackdaw, magpie and rook, among which both birds share the task of gathering the pieces of vegetation which will form the nest. The 'fine tuning', however, the final arrangement of the materials, the shaping of the cup and the addition of a soft lining, may be the female's responsibility. With house martin and swallow, too, both male and female collect the mud which is used in the construction of the nest cup, although the provision of the lining of feathers is usually left to the female. Among all three woodpeckers, as well, the job of chiselling out the nest-chamber in the tree is shared, although not equally, for in the case of the two black and white woodpeckers the male is often far more industrious than the female, sometimes working for several hours at a time while she merely watches from a tree nearby.

Among the other birds that are seen in gardens the major nest-building responsibility falls to the female; this group comprises the tits (excluding the long-tailed), nuthatch, robin, redstart, song thrush, mistle thrush, blackbird, willow warbler, chiffchaff, dunnock, pied wagtail, spotted and pied flycatchers, sparrowhawk and the finches. For the most part, though, the cock takes an active interest, making regular visits to check how things are progressing, and may travel to and fro close beside the female as she gathers materials. In fact, there have been cases of the males of these species doing some of the fetching and carrying.

The wren's system is quite different and unique among British garden birds. The cock wren builds several nests scattered around the territory and then escorts the hen-bird as she inspects each one in turn. Eventually she chooses the one which suits her best for her first brood (although one or two of the others may be used for a second or third brood) and she then places a soft lining of hair or feathers inside.

In any one year, among several species, there will be some individuals who do not build or excavate a new nest but simply use an old one after a little tidying up (woodpigeon, house sparrow, house martin, swallow, swift, blackbird, rook and green woodpecker, for example). Also, there are species which never build a nest, two of which, the kestrel and tawny owl, merit consideration here. The tawny owl merely chooses a suitable large hollow, usually in an old tree, and lays the eggs in the bottom of the hole. No materials are used and no nest is formed. The kestrel, in common with all falcons, follows the same pattern. Often the eggs are laid on the soft base of a large tree-cavity such as the tawny owl might use, but a kestrel is just as likely to take over an old crows' nest in a tree, a soft 'scrape' on a cliff ledge or, as already mentioned, on a

tall man-made structure. It is worth mentioning, in passing, that the sparrowhawk does build a nest: a platform of twigs placed in the fork of a tree or on a group of sturdy branches, usually, but not invariably, high above the ground. Though a shy and secretive bird in many ways, the sparrowhawk is increasingly found nesting very close to roads or busy footpaths.

The period of nest-building is intriguing and, sometimes, mystifying for the bird-watcher. It is amazing how quickly a bird can build its nest without being detected. The behaviour of birds at this time can be quite puzzling. Sometimes the choice of nest-site is patently wrong-headed, with the birds opting for unsuitable or even dangerous sites in preference to others that look (to a human) infinitely preferable. Other birds abandon a half-built nest for no apparent reason. A pair of blue tits which began to use a garden nest-box suddenly, inexplicably, switched their attention to a hole under the roof tiles of the house a very short distance away. They only returned to complete the first nest when the hole in the roof was blocked up before any eggs were laid.

There are other mysteries which cannot be explained, such as the habit, among tits, of repeatedly tapping the entrance to a nest-hole. This has been explained as part of the hen-bird's survey of the property whereby she ensures that it is not damp, leaky or vulnerable to attack and that the wood is sound. Still, this does not explain why she repeats the procedure over and over again, nor why tits sometimes chip pieces away from the entrance hole of the 'correct' size on a perfectly sound nest-box.

As well as many such puzzles, there is invariably humour. Hole-nesting birds frequently attempt to take huge items, such as long strands of grass, or twigs, through a small entrance hole and may spend a great deal of time before they eventually succeed. One female robin entered the lounge of a suburban house to collect dog's hairs, to be used as nest-lining, from the carpet. One jackdaw, which was keen to line its nest with hairs, attempted to gather donkey's hairs from the back of a donkey while they were still attached!

CHAPTER 3

EGGS AND
YOUNG BIRDS

EGG-LAYING

We have seen already that the early sexual development of breeding birds is influenced primarily by the increasing amount of daylight which leads to the kind of pre-nesting behaviour discussed in Chapter 2. However, where egg-laying is concerned, temperature is the major determining factor: birds lay their first eggs earlier in the south than in the north and earlier in a warm spring than in a cold one.

The link with temperature is indirect. The hen will lay the eggs when she can form them; this is determined by the availability of food, which is, in turn, dependent upon temperature (in warm spring weather insects and caterpillars develop more rapidly and the growth of plants which provide food for the finches is accelerated). Considering that, in a matter of a few days, a small bird may have to produce a clutch of eggs with a total weight which exceeds her own, it is obvious how important it is for her to be well-fed and healthy.

During this period just before laying begins, the hen-bird (and in some cases the male, too, if he is to take a share in the incubation) sheds some of the feathers under her belly to form the brood patch. This permits her warm body to come into direct contact with the eggs when they are being incubated.

The timing of the laying of the first egg is much more important than the timing of nest-building. As outlined earlier, the length of time spent nest-building can be varied to suit changing conditions. The process can be halted, should for example the weather deteriorate. The speed of the nest construction is variable, and possibly affected by the hen-bird's hormone development. Early in spring, a hen blackbird or chaffinch, for instance, has a less urgent drive to build, so may take over two weeks to complete the task. A week or so later, the activity will be more intense and a perfectly good nest may be built in two or three days. Then, even when the nest is ready, the first egg need not be laid for some considerable time. By comparison with all this, the 'decision' about the laying of the first egg is crucial, because in normal circumstances once it is laid the breeding programme must go remorselessly forward, as long as there is no unforeseen catastrophe. If the first egg is laid too early, there will be young in the nest before there is a plentiful supply of food on which to feed them.

The various times when different species can raise young is related to the kind of diet they will feed their nestlings. Mistle thrushes, song thrushes and blackbirds can lay early because they are able to feed their offspring earthworms, snails, slugs, insect larvae and berries in the early weeks before caterpillars are available. Even so, if a female thrush or blackbird is prompted to nest too early by a brief period of warm weather in late winter, she may find difficulty in feeding the brood should the weather turn very cold again: the ground may be hardened by frost so that worms are virtually unobtainable and the colder conditions mean that she has to spend longer covering the nestlings to keep them warm, so reducing the time available for foraging.

Robins, chaffinches and tits lay their eggs a little later so that their nestlings can be fed in May and June when caterpillars are abundant. Yet again timing is vital, for the caterpillar crop exists only for a relatively short period in May and June, and a late laying could mean the young are too late to enjoy these benefits. At this time other birds take advantage of this cornucopia of protein-rich food. The blackbirds and thrushes, possibly feeding their second broods by now, change to caterpillars; woodpeckers and tree-creepers feed their young many caterpillars as well as insects and larvae extracted from tree-bark and dead wood. Then, a little later, as the caterpillar population dwindles, redstarts and pied flycatchers provide a mixture of caterpillars and insects for their youngsters, while young greenfinches, goldfinches and bullfinches receive a few caterpillars mixed with regurgitated seeds. These seed-eating finches, like woodpigeons, go on breeding long after those other species which are dependent on caterpillars, as do spotted fly-catchers which thrive on an abundance of flying insects in mid-summer. The same is true of the swallow and house martin which may still be feeding young in the nest in September, or, in the case of the house martin, even in October.

For the majority of garden birds, the pattern of egg-laying is roughly the same: the hen lays one egg per day until the clutch is complete and, as laying usually takes place early in the morning, it is possible to trace the progress of laying by inspecting a nest later each day. Virtually all the garden birds wait until the last or last but one egg is laid before they commence incubation. In the week or so when the eggs are being laid, and before incubation begins, the hen makes only infrequent visits to the nest and may stay away all day, only returning there in the evening to sleep on the eggs.

Much of the sexual behaviour seen earlier is still in evidence during this period and, in many cases, it is at its most intense. Among those birds which indulge in 'courtship' or 'nuptial' feeding, the male will bring food to his mate, sometimes in considerable quantities, thereby helping her to form the eggs while at the same time possibly strengthening the bond between them. Copulation will also take place, having commenced while the nest was being built.

Most small birds copulate several times a day, perhaps two or three times in a matter of a few minutes, although the act itself lasts only for a few seconds. There may be a brief display before and after, depending on the species, but for several garden birds coition is indulged in quite dispassionately, almost as an afterthought, while the two birds are foraging for food or collecting nest materials. The larger birds, such as crows, magpies and birds of prey, mate less frequently, most of them only once a day. Nevertheless, whatever the size of the bird, the period in which copulation takes place extends from a few days before the first egg is laid until shortly after the clutch is complete. It is unlikely to occur at any other time, unless there is to be another brood when it will recur a short time before the next clutch is started.

For a few of the garden birds, the pattern of laying and incubation is rather different from that outlined above. Female swifts, corvids, tawny owls and birds of prey lay their eggs at two- or three-day intervals rather than every day; and incubation commences, usually, well before the clutch is completed, often after the first or second egg is laid. The eggs, therefore, are at different stages of development and hatching takes place over a period of several days. The chicks in these broods look quite different throughout their stay in the nest, their respective ages being very apparent from the variation in size and plumage development. There may be a difference of up to two weeks or more between the first to hatch and the last and their first flights will accordingly be spaced out over a period of several days.

The reason for this staggered hatching is quite simple. Unlike the majority of garden birds, which have little difficulty finding enough food for their young in a normal breeding season, these birds cannot always rely on a consistent supply; so there is a risk, in times of food shortage, of the young birds in the nest weakening and dying. If the nestlings were all of the same age, they would compete on an equal footing for the limited quantities of food being brought to the nest, and if this proved inadequate for the entire brood then they would all die. Yet the food supply might be sufficient to support at least one or two of the chicks. Among young birds which have not hatched simultaneously, there will be a bigger, stronger nestling which will dominate its younger fellows and claim most or all of the food, so ensuring that at least one of the brood survives. If there is slightly more food, the second oldest will be next in the pecking order and will make certain that it survives as well. In times of plenty the whole brood will survive. Thus, these species can expect to fledge at least one youngster.

PROTECTION OF EGGS

Birds have the great advantage of flight, enabling them to avoid danger and to travel great distances in search of food. Unlike many creatures which carry their eggs inside their bodies, however, birds must deposit them in a relatively vulnerable place and leave them there. Here they are much sought after by a number of birds and mammals. The subject of nest predation is dealt with more fully in Chapter 4, but magpies, jays, crows, cats, weasels, squirrels, mice and possibly foxes and mink are the biggest threats.

The different bird species have evolved a number of ways of protecting their eggs to ensure that their line continues. We have already noted that many of the birds greatly improve their chances of successful breeding by choosing a hole in which to nest; keeping their eggs out of sight reduces the chance of detection and a small entrance hole in a tree excludes all predators that cannot fly, climb or enter small holes. So it is not surprising that the majority of garden birds that nest in holes, where the eggs are safely hidden from view, lay light-coloured and very colourful eggs. Pale eggs have the added advantage of being visible to the incubating bird in the gloom of the nest-hole.

All of the garden tits, the treecreeper and the nuthatch lay very pale cream or white eggs with a few small pink or orange-red speckles on them. The three woodpeckers and the tawny owl lay pure white ones and among the most colourful of eggs are the bright plain sky-blue eggs belonging to starling, pied flycatcher and redstart. All these are safely out of sight in a dark cavity. The robin's creamy-white eggs with orange-red speckles are also inevitably extremely well concealed in a crevice or hollow or among the roots of a tree. Other pale eggs are placed in domed or spherical nests. The house martin's are pure white, those of the wren, willow warbler, chiff-

chaff and long-tailed tit off-white with a light sprinkling of small spots.

Birds which build open nests have to use leaves and other vegetation to conceal their eggs. Those that are laid in early spring before trees and bushes are in leaf are particularly susceptible to predation; so, more often than not, they are located in an evergreen such as a garden cupressus tree, laurel, cotoneaster, pyracantha or holly. Dunnock, blackbird and song thrush often choose such a site for their early nests.

A few eggs in open nests are light in colour. Those of the woodpigeon and collared dove, for example, are pure white and are laid on a flat platform of twigs. They are without even the limited protection afforded to the eggs of other birds by the sides of the nest. The bright blue eggs of the dunnock and the greeny-blue, black-speckled eggs of the song thrush are also surprisingly bright for birds which do not make enclosed nests. These species, therefore, although their nests are usually well secreted, not surprisingly seem especially prone to egg-predation.

Most other garden birds that construct open-cup nests have eggs with muted colours often covered with a variety of blotches, streaks and speckles so that the outline is broken up and the eggs merge with the background, the base of the nest. The eggs of spotted flycatcher, blackcap and nightingale, for example, are light brown or grey-brown, whereas those of several finches, goldcrests and blackbirds have soft colours with streaks or darker scribblings. As only dappled light filters through the foliage onto the nest, they can blend in extremely well.

A few birds hide their eggs when leaving them for a while. The goldcrest will bury them amongst the soft lining in the nest so that, to all appearances, the nest is empty. Surprisingly, this is a ploy also used by blue, great and coal tits—surprising because their nests are always placed in holes so the eggs are never visible from outside. This is something worth remembering: the unwary person inspecting a garden nest-box may not realise that there are eggs in the nest. At the very least this may result in a wrong calculation, at worst, in accidental damage to the eggs.

The behaviour of the two birds around the

For a bird which builds an open nest the dunnock lays surprisingly brightly-coloured eggs. Here a cuckoo has laid an egg in a dunnock's nest. Cuckoo eggs usually resemble those of their host but, in Britain, they cannot match the lovely blue of a dunnock's egg.

nest-site contributes to the concealment as well. The nest is built very discreetly, often so quietly that the owner of the garden is quite oblivious of its existence until some time later when a parent bird is seen with a beak full of food.

Even if the nest is detected by a predator, all is not lost. For, as we have seen, many nests are extremely difficult to reach. The house martin's nest, beneath the eaves of a house, is well out of reach of almost any predator, and other nests such as those of goldfinches and goldcrests may be placed on a very flimsy branch which many mammals and large birds would find difficult to negotiate. A similar effect is achieved if the nest is amongst thorny branches, which will deter mammals. Blackbirds, long-tailed tits, dunnocks, bullfinches, chaffinches and goldfinches are all likely to nest in brambles, hawthorn or gorse.

Once the incubation period has begun, there are only short spells when the eggs are left uncovered, so the incubating bird needs to be inconspicuous. It is no accident that the female of a species is often duller than the male. If the hen has to incubate in an exposed site (as in the case of ducks, where the drake is very often extremely colourful) she will be far less conspicuous. As far as the garden birds are concerned, the male is rarely much brighter than his mate, but in the few cases where there is a marked difference, such as chaffinch, bullfinch, redstart and pied flycatcher, the female does all the incubating (although the last two have evolved the use of nest-holes to make doubly sure). In some cases, both sexes are brightly marked: blue tit, great tit, nuthatch and all three of the woodpeckers. These are all hole-nesting birds.

The pale or colourful parts of a bird are rarely on the back; so when it is incubating on an open nest, only the dull back and head are visible. The pale breast of a thrush, the creamy underparts of a spotted flycatcher and the red chest and throat of the robin are all almost completely hidden from view when the bird is observed on the nest. Even if the hen-bird is quite colourful, such as female bullfinches and goldfinches, the dullest parts are, again, on the back. These two birds have another advantage in that they nest rather later than the less colourful thrushes so usually have a good screen of leaves to give their nests additional seclusion. In fact, these are just two of the many species (robin, wren, chiffchaff, willow warbler and blackcap are others) that possess extraordinary skill in the concealment of their nests.

INCUBATION

Among the majority of garden birds, the responsibility for incubating the eggs is the female's alone. Robin, blackbird, song thrush, mistle thrush, the tits, the finches, treecreeper, nuthatch, redstart, pied flycatcher, wren, swallow, willow warbler, goldcrest, chiffchaff, pied wagtail and the corvids all fall into this category. On rare occasions, a male might help out for short periods, but normally his task is to keep guard, protect the territory and, perhaps, periodically visit the female on the nest.

However, in the case of many other species, the cock bird shares the incubation. These include, of the garden birds, house martin, swift, house sparrow, tree sparrow, dunnock, starling, blackcap, spotted flycatcher, pigeons and doves, woodpeckers, black-headed gull and kestrel. It is not always an even division of labour. The male often takes relatively short stints; some individuals may do none at all. The male woodpigeon merely relieves his mate for a short period each day. By contrast, a male woodpecker often remains on the eggs for longer periods than his partner and incubates them overnight.

When one bird replaces the other on the eggs, the 'change-over' may be instigated by the sitting bird, which will leave the eggs and call to its mate nearby. Sometimes, the waiting bird merely arrives at the nest, thus prompting the other to depart. The change-over at a woodpecker's nest is slightly different. The bird that is not incubating arrives at the nest-hole, looks in briefly and calls quietly. It then slips around to the side of the tree and sometimes taps on the trunk. The bird inside flies out to be replaced immediately by its mate. To a human observer who is attempting to follow the progress of the nest, the change-over is clear evidence that incubation is going on.

The length of the incubation period is fairly

uniform across almost the entire range of garden birds. The majority incubate for approximately two weeks or slightly less. Those that need longer to hatch the eggs are mainly slightly larger birds, although the swift can take up to three weeks. Woodpigeon, green woodpecker, jay, magpie, jackdaw and rook require roughly two and a half weeks and crows and black-headed gull a little longer still. Only the tawny owl and kestrel, with about four weeks, and the sparrowhawk with approximately five weeks, incubate for considerably longer.

It is easy to gain a false impression of the behaviour of a bird which is incubating eggs. When a human approaches a nest, the sitting bird will

An incubating bird adjusts its position from time to time and also, as this hen bullfinch is doing, turns the eggs at regular intervals so ensuring that they all incubate properly. It is possible to see that four eggs have still to hatch but that she is also brooding one recently-hatched chick, only a few hours old.

usually 'freeze' until danger passes, so one tends to think of her remaining motionless the whole time. Nothing could be further from the truth. Most birds fidget a great deal, move into different positions from time to time and frequently adjust and turn the eggs to ensure that they are all evenly warmed. The parent bird's head repeatedly turns this way and that as sounds nearby suggest possible danger, although there are times when drowsiness takes over and the bird may well fall asleep for a short spell.

Furthermore, among many species such as robin, blackbird, thrushes, chaffinch, the tits, redstart and nuthatch, the hen leaves the nest at regular intervals to feed, leaving the eggs uncovered for five, ten or even fifteen minutes at a time. Male chaffinches, blackbirds and thrushes will watch as the hen feeds herself, possibly hopping about nearby, but the cock robin, nuthatch and tits will feed their mates at this time. This process can occur as often as every twenty or thirty minutes, but it is usually less frequent than

that, particularly if the weather is cold or evening is approaching.

For most of these birds just mentioned a plentiful supply of food is readily available close to the nest in the territory, so the hen has no difficulty satisfying her hunger fairly rapidly. If food is not easy to obtain or if a considerable journey is involved, the uncovered eggs would be at risk for too long. Therefore, cock goldfinches, greenfinches, bullfinches, and siskins regularly feed regurgitated seeds to their hens while incubation continues. So, too, male sparrowhawks and kestrels, in common with many other birds of prey, periodically bring a kill to the incubating female. Sitting female jays, jackdaws, rooks, crows and swallows also receive food brought to them on the nest. It is still necessary, of course, for these females to leave the nest for short periods to stretch, preen, excrete and possibly to drink.

It is always a temptation having found a bird sitting on a nest to edge closer for a better look. Though many people talk of how 'tame' an incubating robin or blackbird may be, the bird's reluctance to move should not be mistaken for tameness. It is simply that its instinct is to sit tight and remain still: the urge to keep the eggs warm is an overwhelming one and may be stronger even than fear of a human. Only when the intruder comes too near will the sitting bird fly off. Although in many cases the bird will later return and the eggs will come to no harm, such intrusion into the birds' affairs should be avoided at all times. There are some birds which will not readily return and the nest may be deserted. If the bird is kept away for a lengthy period, the eggs will cool and, if a sitting bird is disturbed shortly before nightfall, it may not return in the gathering gloom and the eggs will have chilled by the following morning.

Several garden species attempt to raise more than one brood each breeding season, if there is sufficient food to permit this. Of the summer visitors, chiffchaff, blackcap, and spotted flycatcher often second-brood, while swallows and house martins frequently go on to a third. Of the residents many finches have two broods and robin, wren, pied wagtail, blackbird, song thrush,

mistle thrush and woodpigeon all regularly have two or three. Some pairs of house sparrows raise four broods and the collared dove might manage five in a year. The feral pigeon, incredibly, is capable of exceeding even this number and this species commonly breeds at any time of the year.

On the other hand, most hole-nesting birds in Britain, including the tits, nuthatch, pied flycatcher, starling and the woodpeckers, have one brood only as a general rule; there are exceptions, such as the occasional pair of great tits that second-brood, and in parts of mainland Europe two broods are common with some of these species. In general terms, though, because eggs and nestlings in holes are much safer, birds that nest in holes are able to lay a single, large clutch. Birds that use open nests tend to lay more clutches, and these, on the whole, are smaller than those of hole-nesting birds. The larger birds, like the corvids, tawny owl and birds of prey, all rear just one family too but, of course, their incubation and fledging periods are much longer.

SIZE OF CLUTCHES

There are many factors that determine the size of the clutch, which can not only vary between individuals of the same species but may be different from one year to the next for the same bird. In *British Tits*, Christopher Perrins outlines several factors that influence the clutch size of tits. What follows is based on that analysis, much of which would appear to apply to other garden bird species as well.

The laying date determines clutch size. A slightly delayed breeding season, possibly caused by disturbance, the inability of the birds to secure a satisfactory nest-site, or predation of an earlier nest, will result in a smaller clutch. Clutches laid early in spring are often slightly smaller and, among species that have more than one brood, second or third broods started late in the season are likely to be smaller still.

After a cold winter, in which fatalities among resident birds have been high, there is a lower density of breeding pairs. In such conditions, many species lay bigger clutches, as though attempting to recover their numbers. This may be self-defeating, for a large clutch of eggs does not always result in a high fledging rate or a high survival rate among those that do fledge. A scarce food supply shared between many mouths means that all of the young go hungry. Birds from very large broods are often lighter than those from small broods and a lighter bird is less likely to survive than a well-nourished one.

There may be variations between areas too. For example, clutches laid by tits in gardens are much smaller. There are fewer caterpillars in gardens than in woodland, especially where there are oak trees, so birds which in ideal circumstances feed their nestlings exclusively on caterpillars have to resort to other food, such as aphids, far less rich in protein. If this happens, part of the brood is likely to die and those that manage to leave the nest will be so underweight that they have little chance of survival.

Further afield, variations in clutch sizes occur between different parts of Europe. Among many species, clutches in the south of Europe are smaller than those in the north. In the case of the swift the picture is slightly different. Swifts always lay two or three eggs in Britain, where the summers are cooler and wetter than in other parts of Europe and where, consequently, there are fewer flying insects for the swifts to catch as food for their young. However, in warmer, drier countries, where the insect crop is more plentiful, swifts regularly lay four eggs.

A mature hen-bird will usually lay a slightly larger clutch than a bird breeding for the first time, possibly because she has paired and settled into a territory earlier or perhaps because she has come into breeding condition a little earlier. She is also likely to produce more surviving young from her larger clutch with her greater expertise in the search for large quantities of food for the hungry brood.

Finally, for several tits, another factor is the size of the nest chamber and this may well apply to all hole-nesting birds that do not excavate their own nest. A hen-bird who has to use a smaller, cramped cavity will probably limit the size of her clutch to suit the accommodation available.

Basically, though, within certain well-defined limits, there is a predictable size of clutch for all

Approximate Clutch Sizes for Garden Birds

BIRD	CLUTCH SIZE
Pigeons and Doves	2
Swift	2–3
Tawny Owl	3–4
Siskin	3–5
Rook	3–5
Swallow	3–6
Blackbird	3–6
Song Thrush	3–6
Mistle Thrush	3–6
Blackcap	3–6
House Sparrow	3–6
House Martin	4–5
Dunnock	4–5
Crow	4–5
Spotted Flycatcher	4–5
Robin	4–6
Tree Sparrow	4–6
Jackdaw	4–6
Jay	4–6
Pied Wagtail	4–6
Greenfinch, Bullfinch, Chaffinch, Goldfinch	4–6
Redstart	5–6
Great Spotted Woodpecker	5–7
Green Woodpecker	5–7
Pied Flycatcher	5–7
Chiffchaff	5–7
Starling	5–7
Wren	5–8
Lesser Spotted Woodpecker	5–8
Magpie	5–8
Treecreeper	5–8
Willow Warbler	6–8
Marsh Tit	6–9
Nuthatch	5–10
Great Tit	5–11
Goldcrest	7–11
Coal Tit	7–12
Long-tailed Tit	7–12
Blue Tit	7–15

of the garden bird species, although the limits may be very wide in some cases. The tits, for example, which are capable of the biggest clutches of all, are also capable of the greatest variation. Blue tits in garden nest-boxes may lay as few as six or seven eggs, while a short distance away, in a nest in an oak wood, another pair may have fifteen or more and clutches of over twenty have been recorded.

It is fair to say that each species has evolved a maximum clutch size which represents the most young that an experienced pair of that species can successfully raise, given good weather and ample food. In normal circumstances, clutches are smaller than this. The table opposite provides an approximate guide to the usual clutch sizes of most of the birds which might be seen in a garden. However, there will always be slight variations from these figures in circumstances such as those outlined above.

HATCHING

The newly-hatched young of all garden birds are helpless, virtually naked and blind, their eyes sealed over with a layer of skin to form grotesque, dark swellings on the side of the head. For their tiny size, they have large mouths and huge digestive organs: they are really extremely efficient machines for receiving large quantities of food and converting that into very rapid growth. A blue tit, which may weigh less than 1 g when hatched, will increase its body weight to about 10 g in the two and a half weeks before it flies for the first time. Young birds need to grow this quickly if they are to survive; the weeks spent in the nest and the days immediately after fledging are the most dangerous they will ever have to face.

Nestlings such as those which have just been described are called 'nidicolous' to distinguish them from the 'nidifugous' young of some other birds (wading birds, ducks and domestic chickens, for example) which hatch with a warm coat of downy feathers and can, often within minutes, see, walk, run, call and even, with a little help from the parents, feed themselves. Nidicolous young can barely move at all for the first few

days, except to wriggle slightly and, most important of all, raise their heads and open their beaks to be fed. They are totally dependent on their parents to bring them all their food, not only while they are in the nest but for some time afterwards.

The entire clutch of most garden birds hatches within the space of only a few hours, although occasionally the process can take two days or, in extreme cases, three. This excludes those species which begin incubation before the last or last but one egg is laid. For them there can be a gap of two or three days between the hatching of each egg, so it may be a week or two before the last chick has emerged.

After hatching has taken place, one of the first tasks for the parent birds is to remove the broken shells, the white insides of which are likely to attract the attention of a predator. Oddly, hole-nesting birds also dispose of the remnants of the eggs even though their nest is usually not visible. The pieces of shell are often carried well away from the area of the nest, although some birds

Recently-hatched nestlings, like these blackbirds, are hardly attractive to look at. When nidicolous young hatch, they are blind, helpless and naked, except for a few wisps of down. The one on the right died soon after hatching.

eat them and a few merely drop them over the edge to lie on the ground below. Unhatched eggs, which are still intact (and which retain their original colouring) are usually allowed to remain in the nest, and it is remarkable how many of these are still in one piece after the young have left.

In the very early days, the tiny chicks lie at the bottom of the nest, huddled together for warmth, unable to hold themselves up. Because they are blind, they only know that the parent has arrived with food by some movement or sound which causes them to lift their heads and 'gape' upwards. Some parent birds call gently on arrival at the nest to prompt the young birds to open their beaks. Others, such as woodpeckers, may stimulate the young to open up by gently tapping their beaks. At this time any noise may cause the young birds to beg for food—the sound of a person moving nearby, the opening of a nest-box lid or even the approach of a predator.

For the first few days, most young birds have a few small patches of fine down but they can still easily die of cold, even inside a tree-hole or nest-box, particularly in the case of a brood born early in spring. They will certainly die at almost any time of the year if a parent bird does not cover them at night. Among some of the crow family, for example, the female hardly leaves the brood at all, day or night, at this stage, and is dependent on her mate to bring food for her and for them. Sparrowhawks and kestrels have a similar arrangement.

Where the majority of garden birds are concerned, however, the female leaves the chicks uncovered for short periods while she searches for their food. Usually, though, she will brood them for a while each time she arrives with food and she may remain there for an hour or more. While this is happening they cannot be fed, of course, so in prolonged cold spells the parents are faced with a dilemma. Birds which make open nests have an even greater problem when it is raining, for the nestlings must not be allowed to get wet. A pair of blackcaps observed over a period of several days in a very cool and showery spell took great pains to prevent any water from reaching the young birds in the nest. As the first drop of rain began to fall, whichever adult bird was nearer the nest would immediately cover the young, remaining there until the shower ended.

During their first few days of life nidicolous nestlings lack sufficient feathering to keep them warm. During the night and for part of the day a parent must cover the young birds just as this female blackcap is doing.

The plumage of this song thrush nestling is in an early stage of development and the wing feathers can be seen just beginning to emerge from their needle-like casings. This young bird was placed back in the nest after the photograph was taken and fledged safely just under a week later.

The female was also seen to drink the droplets which had collected on the leaves above the nest, so ensuring that water would not fall onto the nestlings after her departure.

YOUNG BIRDS' FEATHERS

As already mentioned, the young of all garden birds are born with only a few tiny wisps of down mainly on the back of the head and the upper back. Then, after a few days, in the case of smaller birds, feathers start to grow along certain tracts, initially on the wings and tail, and later on the body, gradually replacing the down.

These feathers look at first like little needles, as they grow within hard tubular cases. When partly grown, the feathers begin to appear from the top of these needles and, as they grow and open out, so the casing crumbles and falls away. The bottom of the nest often becomes lined with a powdery dust made of the bits of the nestlings' feather casings. When a feather is fully grown, the blood supply is cut off and the feather is quite dead.

Nestlings' feathers grow all together, unlike those of their elders which develop in sequence. Unless disturbed, most nestlings will not leave the nest until their wing feathers are at least sufficiently far advanced to permit some form of flight. However, the young of a few garden species, such as blackbirds and thrushes, leave the nest surprisingly early before they can do much more than run and flutter, and when there are still some tufts of down attached to head and back. The young of hole-nesting birds, by and large, can afford to stay in the safety of the nest chamber rather longer, so they are among the birds which can fly well as soon as they fledge. Usually the wings and tails of young tits, nuthatches and woodpeckers are well developed when the birds leave the nest.

This first coat of feathers is worn for a few weeks only, perhaps for as little as three weeks from leaving the nest. During this period, the youngsters are rather dull and often speckled, so remaining relatively inconspicuous—an important factor for their safety while still inexperienced and inefficient fliers. Young robins, blackbirds and other thrushes all have heavily speckled breasts, and young redstarts, green woodpeckers, flycatchers and greenfinches are streaked. Recently fledged goldfinches lack the red, black and white facial markings that they will acquire later and other fledglings, such as sparrows and chaffinches, look like the adult females.

The possession of a juvenile plumage has another advantage for some territorial species, such as the robin. If the young birds had the adult feathers in the early days, they would run the risk of antagonising adult territory holders, possibly their own parents, and being driven off.

Whereas the majority of the smaller birds assume their adult plumage within a few months of birth, many larger birds, such as gulls and some birds of prey, do not achieve full maturity for two, three or more years, passing through a series of immature plumages first.

NEST HYGIENE

Many birds, such as seabirds and kingfishers, for example, make no attempt to dispose of the excreta produced by their young, leaving them to deposit it in the nest or project it outwards away from the nest. For most of the garden birds, however, the disposal of the droppings is an important feature of nest-procedure.

The excreta comes out in a white faecal sac, bundled together into a neat gelatinous bag which can be easily carried in the beak (although this ceases to happen around the time of fledging or shortly before). The majority of garden birds fly off with the faeces sac and deposit it elsewhere. This is not only a matter of basic hygiene but also a security measure, for the presence of numerous white faecal sacs in and around the nest would be as likely to attract predators as the broken eggshells. The parent birds of a few species dispose of the faeces sacs by the simple expedient of eating them; in fact, many birds do this early on when their young are still very small. At this time some of the food given to the chick is passed through undigested so the parents can derive some benefit from eating the dropping. Some birds, such as the green woodpecker, probably always do this, while others do so only on

For most birds the disposal of the nestlings' droppings is an important aspect of nest hygiene. This male blackcap is removing a faecal sac as it is produced.

occasions, carrying the sacs away at other times. Some birds of prey, such as the sparrowhawk, eat the pellets regurgitated by their young as well as their droppings.

Nearer the time of fledging there are fewer droppings and at this time a few species, such as most finches, can be extremely sloppy about hygiene and allow the rim of the nest to become studded with droppings, so it is as well that these nests are usually well-concealed by foliage. Other species, such as the swallow and house martin, remove the faeces only when the young are small, as the nestlings, once they have grown, excrete over the edge of the nest, resulting in a small pile of droppings on the ground below. Starlings and house sparrows also leave the young to their own devices when they are older;

but in the case of the starling the result, rather than a neat pile, is a white mess of streaks and smears below the nest entrance. In woodland, the starling uses old woodpecker nest-holes, and because of the toilet habits of the young it is always possible to distinguish a starling's hole from that of the other hole-nesting woodland birds.

A faeces sac which is produced while the parents are away will usually be removed by the next one to return. If there is a dropping waiting and another produced while the parent is present, the first may be eaten and the second transported away for disposal. With some pairs of birds, one of the two is noticeably more fastidious about nest-cleanliness than the other. The bird with the more conscientious attitude is in most cases the female.

Parent birds regularly probe the nest-cup with their beaks and frequently eat small items that they find there. Swallows do this very often and, as they suffer badly from nest parasites, in common with house martins and swifts, it may well be they are removing some of these from the nest. Likewise, if one of the chicks dies while in the nest, one of the parent birds will usually remove it before it can decay and become a health hazard. If the dead youngster is well grown, however, this may not be feasible, so later casualties are normally left where they are.

DEVELOPMENT OF THE YOUNG

As the young birds develop, the pattern of nest-behaviour changes. For one thing, they can now accept larger items of food; thrushes and blackbirds can feed whole worms and the robin can bring a beakful of caterpillars and insects instead of one at a time. Then, after a few days (for most garden birds about the fourth or fifth day) the nestlings' eyes open, enabling them to look at their fellows and at their immediate surroundings, and it is at about this time that they begin to call. If they are in an open nest they sometimes will be able to see their parents as they approach the nest with food, a sight which soon prompts them all to stretch forward, beaks gaping, calling furiously.

There are differences in the colour of the gape which can vary from yellow in the robin, swallow and blue tit, through orange in the goldcrest, song thrush and long-tailed tit, to pink or red in the blackcap, bullfinch and chaffinch. Whatever the colour, there is no doubt that the sight of a young bird's gape is an extraordinarily powerful stimulus to a parent bird, especially if accompanied by the food call. There have been many recorded cases of birds being prompted by this stimulus to feed young birds other than their own, often of a quite different species. Robins have fed wren nestlings, wrens have fed coal tits and great tits, and young treecreepers have been given food by an adult blue tit. Blackbirds have taken food to young song thrushes and baby blue tits, and one female blackbird was so overcome by the sight of her offspring's gape that she put nest-materials into it by mistake while in the process of building a nest for her second brood! In some of these cases, the parent bird concerned had to

pass another nest *en route* to its own and was merely waylaid. Others came about when a cock bird's instinct to feed young was prematurely aroused while his hen was incubating their eggs. It is not always essential for the adult bird to see the youngster; it may be prompted to bring food by the sound of the food calls alone. The insistent calling of young lesser spotted woodpeckers in a nest-chamber attracted the attention of adult treecreepers, starlings and great spotted woodpeckers, all of which came to the nest-hole to look in.

In one case, the combination of a gape and food-calls had an amazing effect on a nestling. A young pied wagtail, having wandered from the nest, scuttled back when its brothers and sisters were being fed. As it approached, one of the other nestlings 'gaped' towards it and, although the youngster had no food in its beak (and indeed was still fully dependent on the parents for its food), it went through the motions of feeding its sibling still in the nest.

Having deposited some food into one of the gullets, a parent will wait for that youngster to defaecate. When they were very small, the young may have needed a prod from the parent on their anus to stimulate the process of excretion. Now, however, the sac is produced to order while the adult waits. Even when one nestling has been fed and the parent's beak is empty, the food-calls of the young continue in the hope that there is more food forthcoming as long as the adult bird remains there. When the parent flies off, the brood immediately subsides back into the nest to await the next delivery.

When lying still, nestlings have a very glum look; the large flanges at the side of their gapes give their beaks a sad, downward turn at the corners, rather reminiscent of a clown. Yet, at the first sign of the parents' return, they are once more galvanised into animation.

During this middle period of the stay in the nest, nestlings become increasingly active while the parents are away. They may be caused some discomfort by nest-parasites and a great deal of fidgeting and scratching goes on. In addition, some irritation appears to result from the growth of their first feathers, which have to be carefully

tended as they will be so important to the birds once they leave the nest. There is also a growing problem of space, or the lack of it, so these activities are indulged in by a kind of rota system. While one nestling is stretching, scratching or preening, the others are squashed together in the bottom of the nest and often trampled on by the active bird who will then receive the same treatment when his fellows take their turn. Nestlings show scant regard for the comfort of their nestmates. It is very much a case of survival of the fittest and, as soon as a parent bird reappears, the young all compete strenuously for the food. If one or two have been sleeping, they are suddenly wide awake and any preening ends abruptly. A nestling which does not call long and hard will not be fed and, therefore, will not survive.

At this stage in their development, the young may still need to be warmed by the parent bird at intervals on cold days and at night, although this is less urgent in a hole-type of nest. The length of time that the parent sits on the nestlings at each session will decrease as they grow and their feathers develop. Sometimes the hen-bird may become quite 'broody' and attempt to cover the youngsters, even when it is quite unnecessary; but when this happens the young usually wriggle out from underneath her and begin calling for food again.

Whereas in the early days, when blind, young birds were unaware of danger, they soon acquire an instinct for self-preservation: they will now respond instantly to any sudden noise or movement or to the warning calls of their parents by lying flat in the nest so that only the dull feathers on their backs (and a couple of wary eyes) are visible. They will remain lying motionless like this until they are sure that the danger has passed when they will resume their normal activities.

As nestlings grow feathers they have to spend a considerable amount of time caring for them. These willow warblers, in the later stages of their time in the nest, fidget and preen more and more, and frequently stretch their legs and wings. In the lower picture, the chick has just deposited a dropping outside the nest; the next parent to arrive with food will remove it.

When they are a few days old, most nestlings can recognise danger. If they sense that they are being threatened or they hear the alarm calls of their parents, they press themselves down into the nest. The same young pied wagtails will eagerly call for food when the parent is seen approaching.

FEEDING

As the young birds have to grow and develop in a very short period of time, they need to be given extremely large quantities of rich food. In a single day, a pair of blue tits can bring over 500 caterpillars to their nestlings, as much as 50 meals a day for each individual in an average-sized brood. In the $2\frac{1}{2}$ weeks that the young are in the nest, over 10,000 caterpillars may be eaten. A small bird, such as a wren or a tit, can make between 400 and 500 visits to the nest in one day when the feeding of the young is at its peak (which for most birds is in the middle period of their time in the nest).

In most cases, the food is carried to the nestlings in the beak. Tits usually bring only one or two caterpillars at a time; but some other birds, such as great and lesser spotted woodpeckers, can manage several in their beaks at once, which is obviously an advantage in terms of saving both energy and time. Sometimes, parent birds arrive with so many caterpillars in their beaks that it is difficult to imagine how they pick the later ones up without dropping those they have already collected.

One of the messiest eaters is the starling. A clumsy character at the best of times, the parent starling is quite likely to lose its foothold on the tree or building in which it is nesting or drop the food onto the ground. One parent bird on occasions managed to miss the mouth of its nestling which was eagerly waiting for food at the entrance to the nest-hole. More of the food went into the nest-chamber than into the young starlings!

A few of the garden birds feed their nestlings by regurgitation. As already noted, the corvids and hirundines transport food stored in their gullets. The finches, too, carry a kind of mash comprising mainly seeds (mixed with insects and caterpillars earlier in the season). The bullfinch actually develops, for the breeding season, a pouch beneath its lower mandible in which it can ferry quite large quantities of food to the nest.

Indeed the great advantage of this method is that more food can be carried each journey and, consequently, fewer journeys are necessary. Whereas the two black and white woodpeckers arrive at the nest with a beakful of caterpillars every few minutes, the green woodpecker makes only two or three trips an hour. The food is stored in the bird's gullet and, inside the nest-chamber, regurgitated over a period of several minutes, so that each youngster has several meals during a single visit, the equivalent of the amount the

The task of feeding the young is undertaken by both male and female of the species. Here, a male great spotted woodpecker (distinguished from the female by the red on the back of his head) is bringing food to his nestlings. This nest was in a decaying cherry tree a few metres from a suburban house in a garden.

other two woodpecker species provide in the course of several journeys.

The use of regurgitation is especially useful to those species that make longer journeys in search of food. The swift is a case in point. Because this bird catches flying insects which, in poor weather, may be scarce in the area around the nest-site, long journeys, sometimes of several hundred kilometres, may be necessary to obtain sufficient food. As the insects are caught in the swift's gape, they are formed into a ball of food in a throat pouch. The young swifts, who can remain torpid in the nest without food for several days at a time, are then fed one large ball of food each.

There are variations, as always. The female crow, for example, who remains at the nest to keep her small nestlings warm, receives regurgitated food from her mate before regurgitating it again for her chicks. Pigeons and doves convert seeds in their crop into a rich fluid known as 'pigeon-milk', which the young drink from their parents' bills. Some species include water in the mash of seeds and insects so that the chicks receive a drink as well as a meal and tiny pieces of grit may be included to aid digestion.

Although there are species of birds where the feeding of the young is left entirely to one or other of the parents, garden birds are rather more democratic, for generally both birds have a share in the process. Even in those cases where the hen-bird has done all the incubating, the male is always on hand to help with the feeding as soon as the eggs hatch.

The pattern can vary slightly between individuals of the same species if one of the two adults is rather dilatory, and in some species one of the birds may have a bigger role to play than the other. The female lesser spotted woodpecker, for example, may leave the bulk of the feeding to the male. Where song is a very important part of a bird's behaviour, as with the blackbird, blackcap, wren, chiffchaff and willow warbler, a cock-bird may spend long spells singing and guarding his territorial borders while the female continues feeding.

In the event of the death of one of the parents, the remaining partner will often attempt to feed the young alone, not infrequently with complete success, although the task may be too great and birds are known sometimes to desert the young in such circumstances. Usually, the loss of the male bird is less serious because among most species of garden bird the hen not only provides more of the food but also carries out the vital role of keeping the chicks warm at night. If the hen dies, the cock will not automatically take over this side of her duties, so even though he continues to bring food to the nest during the day the nestlings, if small and unfeathered, will die in the night.

For a brood of very small sparrowhawks the loss of either parent could prove fatal. The male brings virtually all the food to the nest, so if he perishes the female will have to leave her brood to find food herself and they may die without her warmth. If the female dies, the male will still bring food to the eyrie but he is not programmed to feed it to his young. Instead, he drops it in the nest or on the rim. If the eyasses are too small to feed themselves they will starve when ample food is within easy reach.

The wren is also an interesting case. We have already seen how the cock bird builds several nests; he may also have more than one hen so that when the young are being fed he may divide his time between singing, warding off invaders, possibly building more nests and perhaps even courting yet another female.

In some cases, a brood may be fed by more than the two parent birds, usually among gregarious and sociable birds such as house martins. Long-tailed tits, in the event of a breeding failure, will assist with the feeding of the young at another nest-site nearby.

DEFENCE METHODS

Nest predators in country areas are more numerous and varied than in suburban gardens, where stoats, weasels, mink and foxes are unlikely to be a major threat. In most gardens these mammals are replaced by the domestic cat, by far and away the greatest threat to garden birds. As well as actually destroying nests, cats indirectly cause the death of many nestlings, for when a cat catches an adult bird between April and July it

Blackbirds and other thrushes can feed earthworms or berries to their young, so they are able to nest earlier than many other birds before the main caterpillar crop is available.

probably means that some nestlings in a nearby garden will starve.

The main aerial threat to nestlings comes from the corvids. Open-type nests are often located by jays, crows and magpies, who will take young birds and either devour them on the spot or carry them off to feed to their own nestlings.

Nests in holes and nest-boxes may be at risk too. Weasels can enter the smallest hole, squirrels can enter larger holes and another predator, the great spotted woodpecker, will easily open a nest with its powerful bill to get at the young inside. Starlings are also guilty of taking young. By perching on the outside of the tree or nest-box, with its long beak a starling can pluck out the young birds as they approach the hole to receive food from what they think is their parent.

We have seen how birds have evolved certain methods of protecting their nests while they

When a parent bird arrives with food, the nestlings compete furiously, calling, beaks agape. These young song thrushes are large enough to reach upwards some distance so the parent has to stretch even higher to feed them.

contain eggs. When the eggs have hatched, the problems are even greater for, unlike eggs, young birds tend to move about, make a noise and have to be left unprotected far more often. They are now regarded as tasty delicacies by even more predators. Yet, from the numbers of birds in the garden, it is obvious that many survive. How, then, do they manage to combat all the dangers?

One way, of course, is by their choice of nest-site. Birds which produce more colourful young, such as blue tits, great tits, nuthatches and woodpeckers, must lay their eggs out of sight in holes in trees or nest-boxes. By contrast, young birds in open nests are invariably dull in colour, usually brown or grey, and they may be streaked or mottled to give them an almost cryptic appearance. Any light areas of plumage such as wing-bars or tail feathers are hidden from view as the birds press themselves down into the nest-cup at the slightest sign of danger.

Nestlings in open nests are also much quieter than those in hole-nests. Young blackbirds, though much bigger than young blue tits, for example, make far less noise when calling for food—such a gentle sound that it is barely audible to the human ear only a short distance away, whereas young blue tits in a nest-box may be heard a couple of gardens away. Furthermore, most nestlings in open nests call for food only when the parent bird is present; they place their trust in the adult who would not have ventured near if danger threatened. Young birds in holes and nest-boxes, on the other hand, may call from the relative safety of the nest even when the parents are away. Tits, starlings and pied fly-catchers do this in the later stages of their development, whereas young lesser and great spotted woodpeckers may keep up an almost non-stop din from quite early on. At any one time, there is at least one young woodpecker calling and a continuous hunger-cry is maintained.

An added safeguard is provided by the alertness and wariness of the parents. Except for birds such as house martins and swallows who, happy in the knowledge that their nests under the eaves of a house or on high rafters inside a building are safe from most predators, can sweep straight in to feed their young, most of the garden birds show extreme caution and a degree of slyness in their approach to the nest. Even when there is only one route in and out (through a hole, door or window of a building) the incoming bird will invariably have a good look round from a vantage point before he or she flies in. If danger is near, the visit will be postponed; a bird carrying food for the nestlings may drop or eat it while waiting for danger to pass. If a dunnock or blackbird is nesting in a hedge or bush in the garden, notice the somewhat circuitous route it takes on the way to the nest. The line of approach is not straight towards that section of the vegetation where the nest is sited; instead the bird usually enters a short way away and, when out of sight, works its way through the foliage until the nest is reached. Such stealth is shown even by birds which in other circumstances may be quite tame or brash. For example, the blackbird is a fairly noisy member of the garden bird fraternity, but near its nest it is extremely quiet, going about the business of feeding its young usually in complete silence.

Birds with young in the nest are given to noisy outbursts near the nest only if it is threatened. The loud sustained clucking or 'chinking' of an anxious blackbird is familiar, a warning of imminent danger not just to its own kind but to the other garden birds as well. They will all join in with their own alarm calls, the tits with their churring, the wren with its continual loud buzzing and the robin with its repeated ticking. Such behaviour is an important part of the bird's defence. The warning calls tell the young to lie still; they warn other birds in the vicinity that danger is near and may create a sufficient distraction to cause the predator to forget what it was looking for.

Many of the garden birds will, in fact, go even further than this and put on a 'distraction display' for the benefit of a potential predator, human, feline or otherwise. The anxious parents flit to and fro suicidally close to the intruder, the intention being to persuade it to launch an attack in their direction and not at the nestlings. A robin or pied wagtail may allow a marauding cat to approach to within less than a metre before hopping slightly further off, gradually leading it away from the nest.

With a few of the smaller birds, this distraction display is taken even further with the use of an 'injury feigning' technique, something which is more commonly observed among wading birds and other birds which nest on or near the ground. If the nest is seriously threatened a parent willow warbler or blackcap will flutter on the ground and hobble away as if suffering from a broken wing and blackbirds and thrushes occasionally behave in a similar way. The predator will be persuaded that this is easy prey but as soon as a lunge is made the 'invalid' bird flutters still further off, gradually leading the villain of the piece away from the nest. A human near a nest may be treated to the same display at his very feet.

Sometimes if a nest is threatened, small birds will combine in a concerted attack on a much larger bird like a jay or magpie. Although a direct hit is rarely inflicted, the offender may well be driven away and forced to drop its prize should it have already seized one of the nestlings. Unfortunately, if the chick does not fall back into the nest, it will starve on the ground below or be found by some other predator.

FLEDGING

As the time approaches for the birds to leave the nest, they become even more active and adventurous. There is more preening necessary now as flight and tail feathers form and there is a great deal of flapping of wings and 'practice flying'.

For two or three days before fledging, the young of hole-nesting birds such as tits and pied flycatchers will wait at the entrance to the nest, calling and looking for the parents. Young woodpeckers, after less than half their time in the nest, climb up the inside wall of the chamber and eagerly await their parents' arrival, calling loudly all the while. As the parent bird arrives, the nestling which is at the nest-hole entrance is fed and his hunger satisfied for a short time. He retires to the bottom of the nest chamber to be replaced at the entrance by another noisy youngster who has now woken up and is feeling hungry. During

During their last few hours in the nest, the chicks become extremely restless. Then, usually in the morning, one by one, like these robins, they hop or fly a short distance from the nest, to be found by their parents nearby.

this time tapping can sometimes be heard from within the tree as the young woodpeckers experimentally tap the inside of the tree with their beaks.

Some garden nestlings may half-heartedly peck at what they think is potential food. A loose strand from the nest, a dangling leaf or a small insect crawling around the nest may be tested. A passing fly or butterfly may command the attention of the entire brood. A hover-fly which moved slowly across in front of the faces of six young robin nestlings caused all six heads to turn slowly as one from left to right following its progress—a most amusing sight.

A few days before the day of departure, the young birds begin to recognise the appearance and calls of their own kind. For example, a brood of pied wagtails, five days before fledging, could not distinguish their own parents from swallows flying in and out of the shed which served as a nest-site for both. The young wagtails would beg for food from the adult swallows as they flew past overhead. Two days later, however, they had learned to ignore the swallows and called only to their rightful parents as they entered the shed.

In fact, pied wagtail nestlings are among the most precocious and adventurous of all garden birds. Perhaps because it is a species much given to walking, young pied wagtails may begin to 'go walkabout' and explore the nest and its environs several days before they have developed enough flight feathers to permit flight. Sometimes they fall out of the nest, as a result of their peregrinations, and fall victim to a predator or go unnoticed by the parents and die of cold or starvation, however, sometimes they are able to find their way back to the nest after their explorations surprisingly well. Generally speaking, though, once young birds have finally left the nest they do not return to it; a few birds, such as swallows and house martins, do roost at night in or near the nest from which they recently fledged but most nests, of course, do not afford the kind of protection which is desirable for several birds at night. Hole-type nests may offer such safety but, in spite of this, young tits and woodpeckers are not known to return to their own nest-hole once they have finally made the break.

Just before the young leave, a nest containing a large brood may be literally bursting at the seams. Now any preening is carried out with some difficulty: it is not easy to get the beak to the right part of the right body. As far as defence is concerned, too, many species have an innate mechanism for this time: the young lie still until discovery is inevitable at which time they will 'explode' out of the nest, so ensuring that the predator, although it may catch one or two, will not be able to devour all of the brood as would have happened had they remained in the nest. Even though they can only flutter, there is a reasonable chance of survival if the individuals keep out of sight, perhaps deep in some vegetation, for the next 24 or 48 hours, by which time they may be able to fly and thus their chances of survival will be considerably increased. In the meantime the parents will have found them in their cover and will continue feeding them.

From hatching to first flight can be as little as ten days for a small bird such as blackcap or nightingale. For most of the garden birds, though, a rough rule of thumb, as with the incubation period, is about two weeks. Robin, blackbird, song and mistle thrush, all the finches, house sparrow, long-tailed tit, marsh tit, coal tit, pied wagtail, redstart, pied flycatcher, willow warbler, chiffchaff and dunnock all feed young in the nest for approximately two weeks, although dunnock and blackbird young may leave a little earlier.

Blue tit, great tit, goldcrest and wren take about two and a half weeks to fledge their young. The woodpeckers, collared dove, house martin, swallow, starling and jay take approximately three weeks, and the nuthatch and magpie nearer three and a half weeks.

That leaves only the woodpigeon, whose young are in the nest for three to four weeks, and the tawny owl, kestrel, sparrowhawk, crow and jackdaw which may require up to four or five weeks. Once again, the swift is the truly odd one out: a young swift may fly after five weeks but sometimes does not make its first flight until seven or eight weeks after hatching.

It is significant that many of those with longer fledging times nest in holes and cavities or make enclosed nests, underlining the point that such

The young of some species which make open-cup nests may fledge before they can fly properly. This young blackbird had been out of the nest for two days when photographed, yet it could only hop and flutter and still retained a few tufts of down around the head.

nests are less vulnerable and therefore there is less urgency to get the young birds away.

The final departure of the nestlings can vary from species to species and nest to nest; within a single brood, individuals may choose different methods of departure. A young woodpecker may wriggle out of the hole and begin working its way up the trunk of the nest-tree, whereas a fellow fledgling may fly strongly to an adjacent tree. A young coal tit emerging from a hole between the roots of a tree may hop around on the ground, whereas the bird which follows it may immediately fly up into the branches.

To a large extent, the siting and nature of the nest will determine the method of departure. A young starling leaving a hole several metres up in a tree or building has no other option but to fly, while birds fledged from an open nest have a rather more gentle introduction to their new life. Young birds in open nests will often spend a while perching on the rim of the nest-cup or on a branch beside it before quietly hopping away, one after another, through the surrounding branches. Hidden by the foliage, they can wait nearby for their parents to find them and continue feeding them. In this way, their first flight proper may be delayed for several hours or even two or three days.

Young birds nearly always leave the nest in the morning, giving themselves a full day to learn to cope with the new experience. An hour or two after sunrise is the most common time, once the temperature has risen sufficiently, ensuring that the young birds do not chill when no longer huddled in the warmth of the nest with their brothers and sisters. Cold or wet weather may cause the event to be put back an hour or two or even delayed until the following morning.

Nestlings from hole nests may leave one after another in a short period of time, but sometimes a few of them are reluctant to take the big step.

Starlings, woodpeckers and, on some occasions, tits may leave on different days. At such times the parents, realising that they have two areas of responsibility, continue to feed the young birds which have left while not neglecting those still in the nest. Often one parent will take charge of the group which is out of the nest while the other one continues to take food to the nest. Usually the stragglers will leave the following morning, but there have been cases of woodpecker broods taking four or five days to leave. If the parent bird thinks departure is overdue, it will often attempt to entice the young out of the nest-hole. The visits become less frequent and the young grow more hungry; then the adult approaches the nest-hole with food but quickly flies away, repeating this several times until the youngster flies out to be fed.

Once away from the nest the dangers increase for all young birds. Their flight is not yet very strong and, after a long period of relative inactivity in the nest, there is now a considerable expenditure of energy. The weaker birds quickly become exhausted and fall victim to cats or birds of prey, for whom such naïve birds are easy pickings. In fact, the sparrowhawk nests later than many of the garden and woodland birds so that the time when it has a brood of youngsters to feed coincides with the sudden appearance in the neighbourhood of many unwary fledglings. Also magpies and the other corvids will 'gang up' on young birds, bowl them over time and time again, and, when they are exhausted, kill them. Even medium-sized birds like blackbirds are not exempt from this treatment.

In their favour, however, the young birds have a number of advantages. They have parents nearby who can warn them of danger and they have instincts of survival which prompt them to keep well-hidden in thick cover for much of the time; before leaving the nest they have learned to remain still if danger threatens or other birds give alarm-calls. The time of the year provides them with the maximum amount of leaf-cover and nature has endowed them, for the most part,

with rather drab colouring. Most young garden birds are duller in colour than their parents; the majority are without any bright colour at all. Those birds which are a little more colourful, such as young tits, willow warblers and chiffchaffs, are yellowy in hue, which permits them to blend quite well with the green foliage as they follow their parents through the upper branches of the trees.

Once they have fledged, the young are fed for a while by the parents as they forage for food usually in the vicinity of the nest, as a family group. Some amalgamate with other families and form into flocks. Starlings do this almost immediately the young are fledged and are soon travelling far afield in search of food. In a matter of a few days, probably in less than a fortnight in most cases, the young robins, wrens and sparrows are feeding themselves. Often, in fact, the female starts her next clutch almost immediately and leaves the male to tend to the fledglings. The young tits and specialised feeders like woodpeckers are cared for by their parents for a week or two longer but many of the garden birds are fully independent surprisingly soon after their first flight. Young corvids, however, are wholly or partly dependent on their parents for several weeks, possibly right through until winter.

The young swift, again, requires special mention. Whereas swallow fledglings may be seen perching on fences, telegraph wires and branches of trees waiting for their parents to feed them, young swifts become fully independent the moment they take to the wing for the first time. The parents roost in the nest-hole at night for several days after their offspring have left but, unlike young swallows and house martins, the swift fledglings do not join them there. After a particularly long time in the nest, a young swift is well developed when it fledges and its first flight is probably its migration south. In fact, as the swift spends virtually its entire life on the wing, the young are not likely to touch down again until they return to the nesting colony almost a year later.

CHAPTER 4

SEASONAL VARIATIONS

That birds have held a fascination for man since ancient times cannot be denied. More difficult to establish is the precise reason for that fascination and, no doubt, each of us has a favourite theory. Surely, though, nothing has intrigued the human observer more than the mystery surrounding birds' movements. Where have the birds come from that we are watching? Where are they heading when they disappear from our view? Where are they when they are not in our gardens? There are other seasonal variations to be considered. For instance, what becomes of those birds which do not migrate? What do they do in the winter, and how do they survive?

Despite the availability of high-powered telescopes and radar, as well as sophisticated ringing techniques, we are still ignorant of many aspects of bird movement. Another extremely important seasonal change is moulting, by which the birds replace old and worn feathers with new strong ones, without which survival would become almost impossible. The purpose of the following sections is to give the reader a general briefing about what is already known, or assumed, about the movements of garden birds and moult, in the hope that, armed with this knowledge, he can interpret some of what he sees in his own garden at different times of the year.

It is difficult to generalise, however. Among some species, for instance, a proportion of the population migrates, some make small local movements, whereas others remain in the same place throughout the year. There may be one pattern of behaviour in one part of the country, a quite different one elsewhere; there are even greater differences between what some birds do in Britain compared to the same species in Europe. To complicate matters further, it is sometimes necessary to distinguish between the habits of young birds and adults or between males and females. Variable weather and food supplies can produce still greater diversification and, if that is not bad enough, the same individual may make one journey one year and a quite different one at the same time the following year. The most one can hope to do is to outline some of the principles and to attempt to clarify a confused situation as far as is possible.

MIGRATION

Essentially there are two main categories of migration: firstly there is total or 'true' migration whereby an entire population of a species moves each year between two areas which are geographically separated, using one region for breeding and the other as winter quarters. Secondly there is 'partial' migration when only part of a population vacates the breeding area in the autumn while others of the same species remain there for the winter.

For those birds which are total migrants, the typical pattern is that they breed in the north of their range and spend the winter in the south. For most of our summer migrants, Britain lies within the northern part of the range and Africa or Southern Europe comprise the winter quarters. For a few of our winter visitors, however, like the redwing, Britain falls within the southern or central part of their range.

Most of the 'true' migrants have little choice in the matter of migration: they must fly south for the winter or perish. Even the redwing, although it breeds in the far north, is susceptible to severe cold and many die in winter, even in the relatively mild climate of the British Isles. In the case of the summer visitors, such as swallow, swift, house martin, willow warbler, redstart and flycatchers, the British winter would not provide the insect food on which they depend; for them all, migration is a means of survival which the entire species has evolved.

Why do these birds fly thousands of miles to gardens and parks in damp, cool Britain merely to breed when they could remain in what would seem to be far more congenial surroundings? There is no easy answer, but in tropical or subtropical regions there is greater competition from other birds and an abundance of predators: in Britain, and in Northern Europe in general, there is plentiful insect life in the summer months, ample space for nesting and a limited number of predators.

In the case of those birds which are partial migrants, the picture is far from clear-cut. The conditions in harsh winters are such that those individuals that migrate have a better chance of

The migration of most birds goes unnoticed but movements of martins and swallows are often quite evident and sometimes very spectacular. In August and September hirundines begin to gather in large, excited groups prior to setting off on their journey south.

survival while, in milder winters, there may be a higher survival rate among those birds which remain. Both 'methods' exist because both have proved successful on different occasions. Clearly, if one system proved unsuccessful over a period of time, that pattern of behaviour would gradually disappear as a result of natural selection.

Those members of a population that spend the winter months in their breeding area may have to contend with adverse weather conditions as well as shorter days which offer less time for foraging for food, when food is in short supply anyway. Those that migrate, on the other hand,

face other hazards, which often prove fatal. For instance, they do not know what weather will await them on their journey. They can meet strong headwinds which cause exhaustion, cross-winds which blow them off course, heavy rain and even snow. Large numbers may perish, particularly if they encounter these conditions over the open sea: shelter is unavailable so all they can do is fly low across the waves to reduce exposure to the wind. Although migrants do not normally start a long sea-crossing in bad weather, they can meet adverse conditions at sea having set off under clear skies. Even if they survive the buffeting of the elements, if they are weakened, they may be attacked by groups of gulls which force them down to drown. No-one who has seen a fall of exhausted migrants on the shore, which have just made an arduous sea-crossing in bad weather, can doubt the strain that migration can impose on small birds. In fact, sometimes they are so weak that they can barely move.

There are many other dangers too. For example, some birds of prey feed well on migrating song birds. The hobby, a relative of the kestrel, sometimes flies with small migrants as they head south, periodically picking one off as they travel. However, the most ruthless and cunning predator is man. Thousands of birds are shot or trapped as they fly through Spain, Portugal, Belgium, Malta, Italy and France. Many of them, including robins, warblers, flycatchers and swallows, end up bundled together for sale in food markets. Others are caught to be caged. In Spain, for example caged goldfinches are very common and popular; the majority are kept in cages so small that they can barely turn round.

It is not always possible to tell what is going on when birds are migrating. In good weather many fly so high that it takes radar to detect their presence. In clear conditions they may be travelling up to 2,000 metres above the ground. Often, however, migrants can be seen flying overhead: starlings, chaffinches, swallows, house martins and swifts sometimes move in large numbers which are clearly visible to the observer. In bad weather in autumn, they may pile up near the coast in huge traffic jams as they wait for improved conditions and eventually set off out to sea in great spectacular swarms.

Although the main purpose of autumn migration is to ensure a ready food supply through the winter months, in fact migratory birds leave their breeding area well before food supplies dwindle. It is the gradual reduction of day-length rather than hunger which brings the bird into a migratory state, but weather will often determine when migration begins. Once the weather conditions are right—normally clear skies and little wind, or a light, following wind—the birds can set off.

These are external elements which influence migration; internally, the sex hormones play a part, especially in spring. Because the male's breeding instinct is stronger, the cocks of most species arrive first at the breeding area, often a week or two ahead of the hens. They have to establish territories, possibly select nest-sites and, by means of song and display, persuade a female to stay and mate. Interestingly, in spring, the same conditions in a single location may stimulate contrary reactions from different members of the same species: a resident bird, perhaps a blackbird or chaffinch, might begin nest-building, while an overwintering visitor would be prompted to leave for its breeding grounds further north or east.

Most of our small migrants fly through the night. They may feed for a brief period in the morning of the next day before moving on again but in good weather conditions many birds keep on flying all through the following day, so a large area of land may be overflown. Of course, if a great expanse of sea has to be traversed, this has to be achieved in one stage, although exhausted migrants often land on boats, oil-rigs, light-ships and light-houses. Many more must drop into the waves and drown. Those birds which winter south of the Sahara, that is the majority of our summer visitors, must negotiate those vast inhospitable wastes without stopping in a single, long-haul flight. Swallows, swifts and house martins have an advantage over the other migratory birds for, not only are they specially designed for fast flight, they are also able to feed as they migrate, during the daylight hours, which means that they can rest at night if they wish.

To be able to accomplish these feats of endurance and effort, the migratory birds must feed well and build up great reserves of fat before they embark on their journey. This fuel is stored away in the form of fat deposits. Some of the small long-distance migrants can double their weight in the short period before they depart. On the other hand, the short-haul migrants, such as the finches, need to increase theirs by only about a quarter or even less; these tend to migrate in a series of 'short hops' of about two or three hours at a time, usually in the morning, settling to feed for the later part of the day. They also try to avoid crossing vast expanses of open sea, even if it means making a big detour to do this. Chaffinches, for example, enter Britain from Scandinavia in large numbers in autumn but few take the direct route across the North Sea. Instead they fly due south while on the Continent, make a short crossing from Holland or France and then do a U-turn once in Britain to fly north again.

Redpolls are more likely to nest in birch or alder woods than in gardens, but in winter they roam widely in search of food and often visit wooded gardens. In autumn many British redpolls migrate to mainland Europe. Others move south within Britain.

Other finches, such as bramblings, entering Britain at this time, follow a similar route, which can put several hundred miles on their journey, and goldfinches, leaving to winter in Spain, will also follow a 'dog-leg' course crossing the channel at the narrowest point.

However, finches can cross great stretches of water if they choose, and indeed, in spring, when they return to their breeding areas, they fly by a much more direct route. It would appear that the drive to return to breed is stronger and more urgent than the one which takes them to milder feeding areas in the autumn.

There is no doubt that even those birds which we do not generally regard as specialist long-distance fliers, lacking as they do the refined wings and tails of a swift or a swallow, are capable of phenomenally long journeys. With a following wind, small birds like robins, warblers, flycatchers and even finches, can travel hundreds of miles in a matter of a few hours.

It comes as no surprise, therefore, that birds may leave the mainland of Europe in the morning, fly over the east coast of England in mid-morning and be far inland by midday. So, in autumn, groups of chaffinches, redwings, and starlings may drop down into fields and hedgerows, or even parks, gardens and allotments having entered the country unnoticed only an hour or so before.

Normally, movements are more likely to be observed near the coast, usually when tired birds, often in great numbers, make landfall there in the morning. In spring and autumn, however, there must be few places in Britain, even in towns, over which no migrating birds are flying at some time. These birds on the move may be forced down anywhere by bad weather or they may simply be found feeding in ones and twos among shrubs and hedges in parks and gardens or among fruit bushes on suburban vegetable patches and allotments.

Usually, if it has a choice, a bird will drop down into an area which resembles its normal habitat, and the preferred choice is somewhere offering seclusion and cover. Regularly, every year, however, there are migrants which turn up in the most incongruous of settings. Some birds, like the redstart, are extremely adaptable and are as much at home in open commons or farmland as in woods, parks and wooded gardens. Chiffchaffs and willow warblers, although fairly choosy about the surroundings for their nest-sites, frequently make use of trees and bushes in quite built-up areas when passing through.

How a migrating bird navigates is still partly a mystery. Experiments have shown that birds like robins, wrens and swallows, if removed from their territories or nesting areas to a place some miles away, return within hours to the place from which they were taken. This is the case even when the bird has been transported in total darkness, so that no fixed points or landmarks can be seen. This is an amazing enough fact, but that a swallow can find its way back to the same shed, a house martin to the same eaves or a swift to the same roof-cavity from south of the equator is staggering.

What we do know is that, for at least part of their journey, birds are likely to navigate by certain geographical features: river courses, valleys, ranges of hills, belts of trees and coastlines. These may help in local movements or in the early or late stages of a long flight. As for the major migration, the view that birds are affected by the earth's magnetic field now has less support than it once did, though it is still regarded as possibly a minor factor in certain circumstances. The most popular theory is that the sun by day, and the moon and stars by night, are the points from which a bird can take its bearings. It is evident, however, that this is only a partial explanation—birds can still migrate when the sun, moon and stars are obscured by clouds, although they are reluctant or unable to migrate when it is foggy.

SPRING AND AUTUMN—ARRIVALS AND DEPARTURES

Unnoticed by most people, many birds are on the move long before the first swallow is seen or the first cuckoo is heard. The vast hordes of wintering birds will have begun to drift back to Sweden, Norway, Poland, Finland, Germany, Denmark, Holland, Belgium and other parts of northern Europe: starlings, chaffinches, siskins, redpolls, goldcrests, blackbirds, song thrushes, redwings, fieldfares, jackdaws, rooks, black-headed gulls, and many others. Also undetected will be the influx of returning robins, blackbirds, song thrushes, mistle thrushes, goldfinches, goldcrests, pied wagtails and other partial migrants from the south. They will slip into woods, fields, hedgerows and gardens to take up territories or to pair with males already established there. There will also have been many smaller, local movements of the resident birds as they acquire or reclaim territories or return to old colonies. In December and January, as the male robins begin to sing well, the females leave their own areas and join the males on their territories. Mistle thrushes leave the winter flocks and pair up on a territory while jackdaws and rooks return to their breeding colonies. As long as the weather remains mild, these movements and activities will continue for some time before we think of looking for the first signs of spring, the arrival of the first 'real' migrants.

Of these, the first one which might put in an appearance in a garden is a chiffchaff. Few of these birds breed in gardens but numbers of them work their way through suburbs, feeding as they go in copses, parks and wooded gardens, usually announcing their arrival with their familiar song. One or two males are sometimes heard singing in the south as early as the third week in March and further north towards the end of that month. The chiffchaff's close relative, the willow warbler, is usually heard a week or two after the chiffchaff. Willow warblers make their presence felt by the incessant reiteration of their distinctive and lovely cascading song from the early days of April in the south.

The willow warblers will probably have been

preceded by the first swallows, a few of which appear initially in late March in the south, though considerably later in the far north. Because it is a day migrant and in any case a striking and conspicuous bird, the swallow is the first visual sign of spring to many people. As with most of the migrants, it is the cock which arrives first: he usually pays a fleeting visit to the shed or barn where nesting probably took place the year before and then he disappears again for several days. During this period before nest-building is begun in earnest, as the females arrive, swallows congregate in large numbers at good feeding locations such as lakes and rivers.

At this time, on fine days in April, it is possible to see swallows passing overhead, especially near a river or the coast. It might not be obvious that they are indeed moving north—they may be swirling around in no apparent direction, merely catching insects. Ten minutes or so later, however, the sky will have cleared and the birds will be several miles further on on their journey

to northern Britain or even north-west Europe. These small parties, which may still be appearing as late as June, normally contain many house martins, which arrive approximately ten to fourteen days after the swallows. They often present a similar pattern of behaviour to the swallows: an inspection of the nest-site and then a few days' feeding before nest-building or nest-renovation commences.

From now on, as April progresses, we can look out for other migrants, some of which may make brief 'refuelling stops' in gardens, particularly more wooded ones. Even in towns and cities blackcaps, cuckoos and, slightly later, pied flycatchers and redstarts are regularly recorded. Redstarts, chiffchaffs, willow warblers and, later,

Swifts are among the last summer visitors to arrive in spring. Although a few are seen before the end of April, the majority do not appear until well into May. They are also the first to depart at the end of the summer, setting off in late July or early August.

spotted flycatchers each spring work their way along narrow belts of trees which may border the garden, a pattern of behaviour shared by a number of migrants. The spotted flycatcher, which may not put in an appearance until early May, is, along with the swift, one of the last to reach Britain and may be arriving when other earlier summer visitors, like blackcaps and chiff-chaffs, are already laying eggs, incubating, or even feeding young.

In late summer and autumn, the picture is very similar with basically the same birds (with a few exceptions) calling in on gardens or flying overhead. One difference is that groups of mi-grating swifts, swallows and martins are likely to be seen in greater numbers. Whereas in spring they have spread out and parties have dispersed by the time they reach these shores, in autumn they are still together in groups, which have only recently congregated. Groups of swallows and house martins, tacking this way and that as they move in a southerly direction, are a feature of late summer until they reach a peak in September. Some of these movements may be quite breath-taking as thousands upon thousands of swallows and house martins float overhead, a steady flow lasting for an hour or more at a time. Or they may gather in conspicuous, twittering masses on fences, wires, pylons and rooftops. Swifts some-times indulge in even more dramatic departures. Hundreds fly round the colony, screaming, before they rise up and up and drift away, high in the sky, towards the south or south-east. At coastal sites they may be seen in huge, sweeping catar-acts containing many thousands of birds, flying fast and straight out to sea.

As well as being among the last to arrive in spring, the swifts are the first to leave in summer, spending less time here than any other summer visitor. The young swifts may start leaving before the end of July and the adults very shortly after, often within a day or two. Because they can feed on the wing as they travel, they do not need to wait while they build up stores of fat and most have left by the middle of August. Swifts seen over the garden after that date are probably birds passing through from Scandinavia and points north. The last swallows do not leave until the

end of September or early October while house martins may still be feeding young in mid or late October and there are many records of house martins being seen even in November.

Many thousands of our departing birds in Britain leave far less dramatically and slip away unnoticed. The best chance the garden bird-watcher has of seeing these birds is either during the general dispersal of young, when recently-fledged birds may wander haphazardly in search of food, or when the adult birds are feeding prior to migration. At this time, they may work their way vaguely towards the south or south east of Britain. In late summer, it is worth looking out for willow warblers and chiffchaffs, usually mixed in with roaming bands of tits, foraging in parks and gardens. Many of these are recently-fledged youngsters which have a very fresh lemon-yellow appearance. The willow warblers and chiffchaffs often sing on autumn migration, though it is usually a rather subdued version of the spring song. They are more likely to attract one's ear with their plaintive 'who-it' and 'who-eat' calls.

In late July, August and September, any mi-grating birds which visit a garden may stay a little longer than in spring. Firstly, there is not the same insistent drive to hurry on to the breed-ing area as there was earlier; secondly, there is the need to feed well before tackling the journey ahead; and thirdly, there is more food to be found in most gardens in late summer than there was in April. As a consequence, there may be black-caps, garden warblers and lesser whitethroats feeding on currants, berries and other fruit. Whitethroats and redstarts may join the willow warblers and chiffchaffs catching insects among the vegetation in flower beds and on the vegetable patch. Pied flycatchers leave their nesting areas almost as soon as the young are out of the nest and seem to melt away out of the country,

Pied flycatchers are summer visitors to Europe, arriving in late April and May. They are likely to nest in only very few large gardens in those parts of the west and north of Britain which they favour, but a few individuals pay fleeting visits to parks and gardens elsewhere as they pass through. The male is shown above and the female below.

although there are occasional sightings in parks, cemeteries, allotments, waste ground and gardens. By contrast, the spotted flycatcher, a more conspicuous bird anyway because of its aerial insect-catching technique, is quite likely to pause *en route* and spend a few hours in August or September feeding from the branch of a tree or a fence in suburban gardens.

PARTIAL MIGRATION, SEDENTARY BIRDS AND REGIONAL VARIATIONS

Few people in Britain, apart from ornithologists, think of robin, blackbird, song thrush, mistle thrush, pied wagtail, goldfinch and goldcrest as migratory birds. Because an individual of any of these species may be seen in British gardens in any month of the year, the layman makes the understandable assumption that the species as a whole is sedentary. Surely robins, which are traditionally a part of the Christmas scene, are here all the year round? Well, of course, some robins are in Britain throughout the winter but others are not; and the same is true of those other species mentioned. All are partial migrants in Britain. A closer look at the British robin's movements may be appropriate, partly because it is to many British people the epitome of the permanent garden bird, but also because it shares a number of characteristics with the other partial migrants.

We know that few male robins in Britain leave an area once they have established a territory there. Those that secure a territory in their first autumn, possibly assuming the area vacated by a parent's death, will be unlikely to move far the rest of their lives. For these robins a movement of more than a couple of kilometres is a relatively long journey; many of them will never see any more of the world than the small area encompassed by their territorial boundaries.

Yet, as David Lack has pointed out in his study of the robin, many British robins disappear in autumn and reappear in spring and, whereas some shift only a short distance, others leave the country altogether for the winter months. Almost all of these are females, or young males which have not yet acquired a territory of their own. It would appear that more than half the female robins in Britain leave their breeding areas and either move locally or migrate to France, or even Spain and Portugal.

This pattern, whereby young birds and females are more likely to migrate, is typical of many of the partial migrants. Young robins are unable to compete with dominant territory-owning males while females are less aggressive and less territorially inclined. David Lack also makes the point that female robins which remain behave more like males: they sing, fight and fiercely hold territory. Once again this raises the point that sex hormones affect the migratory urge: in some parts of northern Europe it is only the males of a species which do not migrate while, among most of our migrants, the males move to the breeding area before the females and are in many cases more reluctant to leave if conditions permit them to stay.

Many blackbirds, song thrushes and mistle thrushes spend the winter in France or Spain. It seems that these species are far more likely to migrate from northern areas of Britain than from the south, although the northern populations tend to move south west into Ireland, the southern birds being more likely to move across the English Channel. Probably a small proportion only of blackbirds from the south of England migrate, although, in a cold winter, there may be far more movement as a belt of cold weather drives hundreds of thrushes, as well as finches and other birds, ahead of it. The resulting movement may be in a southerly or westerly direction or it may be random and without pattern as the birds' desperation grows.

Partial migration presents a confused picture. The problem is not eased by the arrival, in autumn, of continental birds to take the place of other members of their kind which have just left. As some of 'our' robins, blackbirds, song thrushes and goldcrests are moving south into southern Europe, so others of their kind are entering Britain from countries to the north and east. As well as birds entering and leaving the country, there are widespread movements within the British Isles. Although large numbers of pied wagtails, goldcrests and goldfinches spend the winter months in Spain, Portugal and France,

Goldcrests can be found throughout Great Britain at all times of the year but, like many partial migrants, they form a fluid population. Large numbers appear to leave or pass through the country in autumn and many cross the North Sea from northern Europe to winter here.

there are others from northern Britain which remain within the country but shift to the south or south-west or to coastal areas. Other species, such as crow, starling, and the thrushes, may also move south and west without leaving this country. It is indeed a confused situation.

On the whole, the garden birds not mentioned are sedentary in Britain. There may be some widespread wandering of feeding parties, as in the case of starlings, or some small-scale southward or westward movement of a few wrens, dunnocks, jackdaws and crows from the north. For the most part, however, the majority of our garden visitors are residents; in other words, if they were born here, the majority will spend the whole year here. This group includes all the tits, nuthatch, treecreeper, all three woodpeckers,

woodpigeon, house sparrow, chaffinch, bullfinch, dunnock, wren, starling, magpie, jay, crow, rook and sparrowhawk, and for many of these birds, not only are we able to say that they do not usually leave the country, we can be confident that many remain within the area in which they were born.

The British house sparrow is so adaptable and has such catholic tastes that it can find food with no difficulty at all, even in the coldest weather. During mid-winter and the time of shortest days, house sparrows have ample time for preening and resting during the middle period of the day. For most of the year, house sparrows forage for food close to their nest-site, apart from in late summer when they may travel a little further to visit the grain fields. Then, they often still return to the nest-hole each night, for the house sparrow is one of the very few British birds which uses its nest as a roost outside the breeding season. Many visit their nest-holes every day of the year and remain faithful to it for life; indeed, for a British house sparrow, a journey of over three kilometres from the nest is quite an adventure.

It is important to stress that these points apply to British birds only, for many species which are wholly or largely sedentary in these islands are partial migrants on the mainland of Europe.

THE WINTER MONTHS

The period between September and April is notable for two reasons: firstly, for the number of birds which arrive in the British Isles to enjoy the benefits of the mild, oceanic climate, and, secondly, for the great variety of birds which are driven by hunger to enter towns and gardens.

It is perhaps not always fully appreciated how many birds invade these islands and other coastal areas of Europe. Most are from countries to the north and east which experience harsher conditions in winter, where the growth of plants and seeds is arrested for a longer period of time and where, because the days are shorter, there is less time for the birds to find the food they need. The birds which make up the vanguard of the winter invasion force will be here in the middle of September but the bulk of them arrive in October or November. Others are still arriving in December or January, especially when the weather is cold.

In numerical terms, the most impressive winter visitors are the thrushes, starlings and finches. Perhaps the most typical winter thrushes are the fieldfares and the redwings which arrive in many thousands, mainly from Scandinavia, and spread themselves throughout the British Isles. The soft 'tzeep' contact calls of the redwings can be heard at night in many suburban areas as the flocks wing their way into the country; fieldfares, which

In recent years, siskins have learned to hang on to peanut-holders at bird-tables. However, although this species breeds in several areas of Britain, it is likely that siskins which appear in British gardens in winter have come from Scandinavia and other parts of northern Europe.

also fly in at night, are silent but, by day, are conspicuous when flying overhead: their distinctive chuckling calls demand attention. In late September and October, migrating parties of redwings (and, a little later, fieldfares) numbering several hundreds can regularly be seen from suburban gardens.

When they first arrive, these two thrushes feed in rural areas, on holly, hawthorn and rowan berries in hedgerows and on the ground in fields, probing the ground for earthworms, snails, leatherjackets and other invertebrates. Later in the winter, when the berries have been eaten and the ground becomes frozen hard or covered by snow, they are forced to move elsewhere, sometimes into gardens. As well as in gardens, during very severe frosts, redwings will feed on the ground on miscellaneous patches of grass, such as lawns, playing fields, even traffic islands, and grass verges where the ground is not quite as frozen as in the more open and exposed fields outside the towns, from which they have come and to which they return as soon as the thaw begins.

Both these thrushes are very nomadic indeed and may wander almost anywhere in Europe. A redwing which winters in Britain one winter may well be found in the region of the Mediterranean or even the Middle East the next year. Similarly, two young redwings from the same nest may be thousands of miles apart by the end of their first winter.

In mild weather the flocks of redwings and fieldfares tend to drift back towards their breeding haunts before the end of winter. In most years, however, there are still redwings and fieldfares in Britain until April but most have gone by the middle of the month.

Winter visits from the other thrushes are less spectacular and may even go unnoticed. Blackbirds arrive here from Scandinavia, Belgium, Holland, northern Germany and Poland, and other countries. Some song thrushes and a few mistle thrushes come here from Scandinavia, Holland and elsewhere; others pass through in autumn on their way further south, for many blackbirds, mistle thrushes and song thrushes from northern Europe are found in southern Europe in winter. As many thrushes migrate at night and can travel several hundred kilometres in a few hours, it is not surprising that they frequently pass by unobserved. In fact, with many migrants, it is only when they are found feeding in the morning that one can appreciate that a movement has taken place.

Of the finches, in most winters, the most numerous immigrants are the Continental chaffinches. Like starlings and redwings, they may leave the mainland of Europe in the early morning and be here in two or three hours. They come from various countries including Northern Germany, Finland, Denmark, Norway, and Sweden, but even those from Scandinavia normally enter the country in the south-east, making a huge detour to avoid a long sea crossing, as already explained. However, these visitors are less likely to be seen in gardens than our local chaffinches which feed in a relatively small suburban area. The Continental chaffinches rely almost exclusively on a diet of seeds and consequently forage widely in open country. In such places they are sometimes mixed with their close relatives, the brambling, a wide-ranging, winter visitor over most of Europe but a visitor to Britain in relatively small numbers from mid-September onwards. Bramblings are most likely to be found well away from towns, feeding on beech mast on the ground beneath beech trees. From time to time they appear in gardens and feed at bird-tables.

Like the redwing (but unlike chaffinches) bramblings may be in Britain one winter but in eastern Europe the next. The same is true of the siskin, which has been known to winter in Turkey or Russia the year after spending a winter in western Europe. Each autumn, from the end of September, great numbers of this species enter Britain from Scandinavia, Finland, central and eastern Europe. The siskins that breed in Britain probably move south as their northern relatives move in, often in the company of many lesser redpolls. In recent years, siskins have appeared with increasing frequency at bird-tables, where they feed on peanuts, hanging on upside down with tit-like agility.

In autumn starlings also arrive in Britain in huge numbers from France, Holland, Belgium, Denmark, Finland, Germany, Poland, Russia and elsewhere. They tend to feed in large flocks in open country and fly to the vast rural night-time roosts, though some move into town roosts each night. Many rooks also make the North Sea crossing to join up with British flocks. They can come from northern and central Europe and possibly as far afield as Russia. From mid-September onwards, goldcrests enter the country to join forces with British goldcrests which have not moved south. Despite their tiny size, many of these birds brave the North Sea, taking the more direct route, unlike the finches, from Scandinavia into northern and eastern Britain. So, too, hordes of black-headed gulls from Baltic and North Sea coastal areas may be found feeding on farmland, open fields and refuse tips. Smaller numbers of robins, wrens, house sparrows, crows, jackdaws, woodpigeons, sparrowhawks and kestrels cross over from northern Europe in the autumn and some stay here probably until spring.

During the winter months, from the end of September until March, British blackcaps are in Southern France, Spain, Portugal or Africa. Those few which visit our gardens in winter almost certainly all come from mainland Europe (Scandinavia, Holland, Belgium and other northern countries) and arrive mainly in the second half of winter. Many over-wintering blackcaps appear to be birds in their first year which have ended up in Britain by accident after a typical, arbitrary, post-fledging dispersal.

Chiffchaffs are among our last migrants to depart in autumn, when they move to winter quarters in southern Europe around the Mediterranean or in Africa. It is possible that a few British birds linger on here but the vast majority have gone by mid-October.

IRRUPTIONS

Infrequently, unpredictably, yet spectacularly, a phenomenon occurs which sends a tingle through even the most jaded birdwatcher and attracts the eye of the least observant householder. Only a few species are involved in irruptions but their numbers can sometimes be such that they force themselves upon our attention.

To understand irruptions we must realise that the natural rhythms of many trees involves a year or two with a bumper crop of fruit followed by a year during which the trees 'rest', when they produce relatively little. So, every few years, those birds which rely on the fruit of trees for their winter food are faced with a serious food shortage, unlike those birds which feed on herbaceous plants, which produce seeds every year. Often this year of dearth follows a winter of plenty which resulted in a high survival rate for the birds and a good breeding season. So the problem is compounded: a shortage of food at a time when the population is at its greatest. Because the trees in an entire region are often similarly affected, the whole population of a particular species must move out and fly to an area where the trees are at a different stage in their 'cycle'.

Irruptions of different proportions take place in some parts of Europe in most winters, the birds most commonly involved being brambling, siskin, redpoll, fieldfare, redwing, blue tit, great tit, coal tit and the waxwing.

Beech mast is rarely abundant in one area for two successive winters, so bramblings and great tits on the Continent may have to leave those areas and search for food elsewhere. Similarly, that mysterious and elusive bird, the waxwing, feeds principally on rowan berries. If berries are plentiful in Finland, the waxwings will not move far for much of the winter but, if the rowan trees are 'resting', the flocks of waxwings must move

Despite its name, the black-headed gull never has a black head. In spring and summer, it sports a chocolate brown head. Outside the breeding season, when it is most likely to be seen in towns, it has just a dark smudge at the side of the head.

on. On such occasions, swarms of them can work their way south and south-west through Europe, sometimes even to the Mediterranean coast, thousands of kilometres from their breeding grounds in the far north, Russia and Siberia. They then move into gardens, feeding on hawthorn, pyracantha and cotoneaster berries, and, like the siskin and other birds from remote areas where man is not a common threat, they can be extraordinarily tame. Every year there is a considerable movement through Europe, when few if any waxwings reach eastern Britain, but in years of irruption their numbers may be multiplied many times and they can then be seen in many parts of the British Isles.

In a given area, a winter in which there were no bramblings, redpolls or siskins may be followed by one in which there is a population of several thousand. A 'siskin winter' in British gardens, therefore, is not a result of bad weather—in snow, tree-feeding birds like siskin, redpoll and some of the tits have a distinct advantage over species which feed on the ground. It is rather an indication that the crop of birch and alder seeds in Scandinavia has failed. The irruptive birds move at random according to the availability of food, and where they find food they will remain until it runs out. Therefore a siskin which finds easy pickings at a bird-table is likely to feed there for days or weeks, and may even prevent other birds from feeding from a peanut-holder on which it is perched.

THE LOCAL BIRDS IN WINTER

Having explained the general pattern of winter movements, we can now take a closer look at the way the familiar garden birds use a garden in winter. There are those birds for whom the garden or a section of it represents part of a defended territory. As we have seen, the most tenacious is the robin. In the first half of the winter all robins, including those females which have not moved away, hold individual territories and expel other robins which intrude. As a result, until December or January, there is likely to be only one robin in a garden, unless it is a large enough garden to accommodate two robin territories (or there is

a boundary between two territories passing through the garden). If this is the case, regular, angry border disputes will be evident.

However, at any time from mid-winter onwards, the males, which have been singing for some weeks, intensify their song and attract a female robin onto their territory, usually from somewhere in the vicinity. From then on, there will be two robins in the garden, until after the breeding season.

No other garden bird is as territorially inclined as the robin throughout the winter, but some wrens and dunnocks hold winter territories in gardens and defend them against other males of their own kind with increasing energy as winter progresses towards spring. Mature blackbirds normally also retain their territory from the previous year throughout winter, although other blackbirds are tolerated for the early part of winter at least. These territory holders, which can often be picked out with careful observation, usually remain dominant over the other birds and become increasingly intolerant of trespassers in the latter half of the winter period.

Of course, there are many variations on a theme. Young blackbirds may wander in and out of different territories or they may take up a small territory or part of an adult's territory in autumn and hold onto it for part of the winter, until ousted by a mature bird (if there is one to do this). In very cold weather, the territorial boundaries break down (except for those of the robin). At such times, blackbirds feed communally and permit other blackbirds to intrude, and wrens may gather in large numbers for roosting. When the temperatures rise again, however, the territorial boundaries are re-established, though it is worth noting at this stage that boundaries can and often do shift; territories alter their shape and size and may change hands several times during the course of one winter.

During the winter months, many of the other resident garden birds remain within a limited area which they are willing to share with others of their kind and within which their separate breeding territories are located. Birds in this category include many tits, nuthatches, treecreepers, woodpeckers, crows, magpies, jays and chaf-

The dunnock appears to be a very sedentary bird and may remain on or near its breeding territory throughout the winter. Like the robin, some dunnocks defend a territory through the winter months.

finches. Although this 'winter range' for some birds includes the local gardens, for others a trip into an area of housing means leaving the normal range, and they will undertake such a journey only if they are experiencing difficulty in finding food.

During winter, many garden birds move around in small feeding parties, which can contain quite a variety of different species. Large flocks of blue tit, great tit, coal tit, marsh tit, long-tailed tit, nuthatch, treecreeper, goldcrest and lesser spotted woodpecker can sometimes be seen feeding in each other's company, for example, though groups do not necessarily include all these species at once. More often only small parties, sometimes comprising just one or two species, visit the bird-table on their circuit.

Perhaps the mention here of a 'circuit' requires a little explanation. Many householders talk about 'their' blue tits, great tits or *the* greenfinch which takes peanuts from the nut basket. However, outside the breeding season, it is just not possible to label them in this way. As already explained, a robin, or a pair of robins, may be permanently in the garden and a dunnock or blackbird may feed there much of the time, but for most of the other birds the garden is only one of many stopping-off points on a wide-ranging feeding trip. In the case of the blue tits, great tits, coal tits and greenfinches, a group will feed for a while in one garden and then move on to another to be replaced by other groups which are doing the same.

A well-stocked bird-table in a well-wooded suburb or within easy reach of a copse or a park may receive visits from several dozen different tits each day. Ringing has shown that over a hundred blue tits may feed at one bird-table in a few hours. Similarly, each group of greenfinches which arrives to feed on the peanuts is likely to be a dif-

Many birds depend on berries in mid-winter when other food is scarce or when the ground is frozen hard. This blackbird is eating hawthorn berries.

ferent one as these birds wander within a given area even more widely than the tits. Although only a handful, probably less than ten, are present at any one time, during the course of a winter, incredible as it may seem, a thousand or more may pass through. By contrast, the nuthatches, marsh tits, woodpeckers, magpies and jays which venture into the gardens from the local woods will usually repeat their visits so that the same birds are seen over and over again.

These birds tend to visit a bird-table in ones and twos, but if one long-tailed tit finds an abundant food supply it will quickly be joined by the whole feeding party. Throughout autumn and winter, long-tailed tits move around in tightly-knit groups, keeping together with repeated contact calls. By providing a regular supply of the right kind of food, it is possible to persuade a party of long-tailed tits to visit the bird-table very regularly indeed. Because they are so vulnerable to cold weather, this may make the difference between life and death for the entire flock. In freezing conditions, they can come

to rely on this food supply to such an extent that they only make short trips away from it; their 'circuit' shrinks and they may return to the food three or four times an hour throughout the day. On such occasions, one can predict the time of their arrival to within a few minutes.

Very frequent visits by a few other species might signify something rather different. Coal tits, nuthatches and jays are known to store food to be eaten on another occasion. If one of these birds leaves the bird-table carrying food in its beak and then returns very quickly, it may mean that the nut or seed has been secreted away in a hole or crevice, or possibly among some vegetation or moss. Sometimes food is even buried in the ground. One nuthatch, which returned many times to a bird-table with earth on its face, had obviously been using this method.

During the winter, as at most times of the year, the greatest amount of bird activity is in the early morning. It is at such times that some of the more timid birds may venture into gardens when there is rather less human disturbance. In one case the owner of a garden containing an old, decaying cherry tree was convinced that some nocturnal creature was attacking the bark of the tree in the hours of darkness. The chipped and splintered wood fragments lying on the ground were proof that something was attacking it in the night. It was only when he rose particularly early one morning that he discovered a great spotted woodpecker savaging the dead wood to get at the grubs and pupae within. The bird had come from a small copse a mile and a half away and, presumably because the garden and those adjacent to it offered little cover, made daily sorties there only when the area was fairly quiet.

Later in the day, it is noticeable that there are far fewer birds at the bird-table. This is because, after a morning's feeding, most of them retire to a perch, usually amongst foliage, to spend the middle part of the day resting and preening. Later still there will be another bout of feeding, the length of the rest period being decided by the weather conditions. In very cold conditions, feeding may have to continue virtually throughout the day, but in mild weather they can enjoy a fairly lengthy rest before another short period of feeding later in the afternoon. Those that have retired a little distance, to the park or copse a mile or so away, are unlikely to bother with another trip back to the suburban gardens until the following morning when they reform into feeding parties and once more set off on their feeding circuit.

As the days lengthen and spring approaches, or in mild spells in the second half of winter, sexual and territorial activity increases and many of the birds spend an increasing amount of time around their future nest-sites and less and less time feeding elsewhere. As fewer birds commute to the local gardens, the numbers at the bird-table dwindle considerably until the majority of the birds seen in the garden are those which are intending to nest there or in the immediate vicinity.

MOULT

Feathers are very important to a bird's survival and much care is taken of them by their owners, as we have seen. Nevertheless, it is necessary to discard them regularly and replace them with new ones. All birds moult their feathers at least once a year; many birds, such as ducks and waders, do so twice a year, one full and one partial moult. The willow warbler undergoes two complete moults each year, one in Europe after breeding and a second in its winter quarters before it returns north again in the spring.

The majority of garden birds replace their feathers once only, in late summer or autumn. Nevertheless, if a feather should fall out at some other time of the year, another will grow in its place. A feather which breaks off, however, leaving part still in place, will remain there until it falls out at the next moult. For the birds which concern us, the annual moult involves a complete refit of all feathers on a 'rota' basis. With small birds in the garden it is not always easy to see that the moult is under way, although they may look extremely ragged. In larger species, such as crow, rook and kestrel, the gaps where wing and tail feathers are missing may be quite visible as the bird flies overhead, silhouetted against the sky.

Although most birds can cope surprisingly well without any tail feathers at all, woodpeckers and treecreepers rely on their stiff central tail feathers for support. Whereas the other birds moult their tail feathers from the centre outwards, the woodpeckers and treecreepers retain these 'support' feathers until they have acquired their other tail feathers.

In most small birds the wing and tail feathers are replaced while the moult of the body feathers is going on, which normally starts at the rump and ends with the head feathers. (Tits have a slightly different arrangement: their wing and tail feathers are moulted usually before most of the body feathers.) Tail feathers are renewed fairly quickly but the moult of wing feathers, which are so crucial to survival, is a much more gradual process, so that the bird does not have too many missing, or only partly grown, flight feathers at any one time. The gradual and se-quential nature of moult ensures that a bird is never left without insulation or the power of flight. However, there are a few species of birds, such as ducks, which lose all of their flight feathers at once and for a period of $1-1\frac{1}{2}$ months are unable to fly.

Most species start by shedding their innermost primary flight feather on each wing, the moult proceeding outwards feather by feather to the tip of the wing. When a few of the new primaries are growing, the outermost secondary feather is shed and the same process operates in towards the body with the growth, one after another, of new secondary flight feathers. One bird, the spotted flycatcher, for some unknown reason, operates its wing moult in a completely opposite sequence to this.

In Europe, most birds moult between July and September, but there are several exceptions to this rule. In a good year, the breeding season may be extended, so moult may be delayed until October or even November. Birds which have not bred or which nested early will moult in June or even, exceptionally, in late May. (There are, of course, variations between regions.)

The duration of the moult varies from one species to another, although there can be vari-ations between individuals of the same species. A bird which starts moulting later than others of its kind, possibly because of a protracted nesting period, will moult more rapidly. Birds which are due to embark on a long migration tend to moult relatively quickly. Generally speaking, though, small birds take less time to moult than large ones, although tits, with a moult which can last as long as 4 months, are something of an excep-tion. A redstart's moult lasts for a mere 40 days or so, a robin's for approximately 50 days and most finches' for 10–12 weeks. By comparison, the jay and jackdaw take 14–15 weeks, and the carrion crow about 19 weeks. The moult of the adult woodpigeon may start as early as February and continue, slowly and surely, until November. Some birds, such as swifts and birds of prey, need supreme powers of flight at all times to enable them to catch their prey, and have a rather lengthy moult so that flying is at no time impaired.

During the moult those birds which have held territories in recent weeks become quiet and secretive. They spend considerable periods of the day just resting and preening. It has been sug-gested that some birds leave their territory in late summer after breeding, and that certainly appears to be the case with a few, such as pied flycatcher. Most, however, are just very inconspicuous. They no longer sing or make regular trips to and from nests or show any territorial behaviour. It is ad-vantageous for them to stay on territory, a place they have chosen for its plentiful food supply and which they know very well. This quiet period is a brief lull only, for by early August or even late July the young robins from the first broods have acquired their red breast feathers and have begun to sing and fight. Two or three weeks later, the adults start to join in and reassert themselves, in most cases reclaiming a territory for the autumn and winter.

Many birds, of course, will be setting off on their long autumn migration so there will be no point in redefining territories. Even though the demands of the moult are small compared to breeding and migration, it does nevertheless use up energy, so it will not take place while the bird is migrating. For most of our summer visitors, it occurs before migration, as with the chiffchaff, willow warbler and redstart. Often the moult is not completed before departure, however, so the bird has to set off still retaining some of its old, unmoulted feathers. It will then suspend the moult until the migration is over and the process will be completed in the winter quarters.

A few species, such as garden warbler and spotted flycatcher, have no moult before they migrate, or at most moult a few tail, body or minor wing feathers. Likewise, swifts wait until they reach Africa for their main moult. Swallows and house martins often continue breeding so late into the summer that they have little time for moult before heading south. They, too, usually replace their flight and tail feathers during the winter in Africa.

Before those summer visitors return, interest-ing changes take place. Several of the birds take on a slightly different look as winter progresses. The black-headed gulls which swoop down into

some town gardens are a prominent example. They have had white heads with a grey smudge by the eye all winter, but now, in the early part of the year, they begin to develop their chocolate-brown heads for the breeding season.

Pied wagtails have a second partial moult in spring and can look much smarter after it, especially the male whose back and rump become jet black instead of grey-black. He also gains a more solid black patch around the throat. Pied flycatchers also have a second partial moult before they leave Africa. However, most birds which assume a new appearance for the spring do so without going to the trouble of growing

Most birds replace their feathers once a year after the breeding season. However, the following spring, they may take on a new appearance without losing any feathers. This male chaffinch, photographed in late winter, is acquiring the familiar blue-grey head and nape as the brown tips of the feathers wear away.

new feathers. A good example is the starling, which has a spotted appearance through the autumn and early winter. As the tips of the feathers become worn away, the white spots disappear to leave the bird with the familiar glossy, green-black uniform. Mistle thrushes may begin to look light grey rather than tawny brown on

94

their upperparts by the same process and the tips of the feathers under the cock house sparrow's bill wear away to reveal a larger black bib. The brown head and nape feathers of most cock chaffinches are also abraded giving the bird a smart slate-blue head. The appearance of the cock brambling, an occasional garden visitor, is transformed as his buff head and back feathers are worn away to become jet-black. Likewise, the cock redpoll's pink chest and the male reed bunting's black head and neck markings slowly appear through the winter as the dull grey tips are worn down.

The Post-juvenile Moult

From June or July onwards, or even before in the case of a few birds from early broods, the young birds which have survived pass through their post-juvenile moult and begin to develop the appearance of adults.

For most of the birds with which we are dealing here, this is only a partial moult. The body feathers are replaced but the flight and tail feathers are large and, therefore, represent a considerable investment in terms of time and energy, so it makes sense to keep them for another year. It would certainly appear to be something of a waste to discard them so soon with a great deal of life still left in them. There are exceptions to this as to most 'rules': the house sparrow, the long-tailed tit and the starling, for example, moult all their feathers in their post-juvenile moult. A few other variations may be found, such as young great tits which sometimes moult some or all of their tail feathers at this time.

Because the young birds only replace some of their feathers, they are able to complete this moult relatively quickly. Young blackbirds, for example, do so in about 5 weeks, while birds from later broods can be even faster. The head, as usual, is the last part of the body to moult and, because this stage takes some time, up to nearly half the length of the moult, householders have a good chance to observe these rather grotesque-looking young blackbirds in the garden with heads like vultures.

Late summer and early autumn can sometimes be rather quiet times for bird-watching in a garden. Yet the observant watcher can detect some interesting details of plumage. Young blue tits, great tits and coal tits may now be independent but they still retain some yellow around the face. Young robins may still be acquiring their red breast feathers: with these feathers beginning to show amongst the dark speckled ones, the bird can look like a quite different species to the novice. The young blackbirds take on the appearance of a patchwork quilt, with their dark feathers replacing the speckled brown ones, and the young starlings look oddest of all as they lose their pale juvenile feathers and grow glossy black ones with white spots. Earlier, in their ghostly-grey plumage with creamy spotted throat they look so unlike their parents that they are frequently taken for thrushes or a different species altogether.

During this time there may be some young birds whose tail feathers have not quite reached their full length. Young swallows are easily spotted, lacking as they do the long tail-streamers of the parent birds. Juvenile pied wagtails are conspicuous by their pale creamy-grey colouring; if recently fledged, possibly from a late brood, they may have tails that are only half-grown. Earlier in the summer, magpies and long-tailed tits with short tails would have been young birds, a sure sign that breeding had been successful.

Until October or November when they moult, young woodpigeons can be picked out by their duller plumage and the absence around the neck of either a white patch or the iridescent blues and greens. At this time young rooks are very difficult to distinguish from crows because of the black feathers on their face; but during the winter months they will lose these feathers and by spring have the grey-white patch on the face of the adult. In the months that follow, the white face patch gradually becomes more extensive as the bird reaches maturity.

The black redstart, a very common bird in towns in some parts of Europe but an extreme rarity in Britain, has an unusual plumage development. The young male of this species usually does not attain his full adult livery until the second year of his life. Many breed in their first spring still carrying markings very like the female's, without a black face or white wing panel.

After their post-juvenile moult, young birds (with the few exceptions which have a complete moult) possess two ages of feathers: those wing and tail feathers which they acquired in the nest and those which grew in late summer in their post-juvenile moult. Throughout the winter, it is possible to tell the age of some of the birds in the garden by close scrutiny. The darker young male blackbirds, for example, still visibly bear the brown flight feathers of their early days. Although some may cause confusion (for their over-all colour can range from the brown of a female to almost jet-black) they can also be told from older birds by the lack of yellow beak and eye-rim. These gradually become yellowish as spring nears but they are not usually bright golden until the next year. Female blackbirds in their first year also gradually develop a more yellow-coloured beak as they grow older.

For the vast majority of the garden birds, the next moult comes in late summer, the year after their birth. By this time most of them will have raised young of their own and will have embarked on the annual cycle of the adult bird: pairing, mating, nesting, raising young and then undergoing a complete moult.

CHAPTER 5

DEATH, DANGERS AND PROTECTION

In the wild, threats to the lives of birds are varied and numerous. A great deal is yet to be discovered about causes of death, but man is undoubtedly adding greatly to the many natural hazards which are encountered every day by garden birds. Nevertheless, everyone who has a garden can do much to combat these different dangers and thus aid the birds' chances of survival.

CAUSES OF DEATH

Birds can die at any time, day or night, for many different reasons: predation, disease, accident, exhaustion, trauma, starvation, bad weather, as well as poisoning, shooting and other human activities. The relative importance of the different causes of death varies from place to place, from species to species, month by month and year by year. Even so, man is probably the greatest single threat to wildlife. Housing requirements, associated industrial development and intensive farming methods have all caused massive destruction

of habitats. The variety of bird species which survive is in inverse proportion to the number of buildings: only house sparrow, starling, pied wagtail, house martin, swift and feral pigeon, and possibly two or three other species, can thrive in a heavily built-up area.

Many birds die as a result of accidents in gardens. Netting to protect fruit is potentially lethal. Thrushes and blackbirds frequently find their way inside the fruit cage and, in their attempt to get out again, become entangled and remain trapped until they die of exhaustion, starvation, or strangulation. Windows can create problems, and there are some which are regularly struck by flying birds. This is most likely to

In the bird world most disputes go no further than threatening sounds and aggressive gestures. Fights that do occur are usually brief and normally between individuals of the same species. Here, however, a blue tit and great tit have become locked together in combat on the ground.

involve windows which face each other across a room. The bird can see light beyond and attempts to fly through, often with fatal consequences. Any window, however, can prove deadly, especially when bright sunlight on trees and buildings creates such a clear reflection in the glass that it looks real. On some occasions, fortunately, the victim is merely stunned. If left unmolested in a quiet place, a stunned bird will often recover and be none the worse for the experience. Collisions of other kinds sometimes occur. Some birds die after hitting telephone wires and power cables.

In urban and suburban areas the most frequent accident, however, involves the motor-car (which, it has been claimed, is the most common cause of death among town blackbirds). Such accidents are most likely to occur in spring and summer, when parent birds take risks and become less conscious of danger in the race to feed their young. If the nest is on one side of the road and the main foraging area on the other, as is often the case, the birds will have to cross the road several hundred times a day. As well as blackbirds, other thrushes and dunnocks are common victims in this way. Later in the summer, too, there is the added hazard of many young and inexperienced birds apparently oblivious to danger on the roads.

Where large groups of birds feed near a busy road, the outcome is potentially disastrous. In winter, roadside beeches, for example, attract huge flocks of chaffinches and bramblings which feed on the beech mast on the ground and swirl across the road in great clouds if startled by a noisy motorbike or lorry. In one case, twelve fresh brambling corpses were found within a few metres of one another.

Usually, it is impossible for the driver of the car to avert the collision, so suddenly does the bird appear and strike the car. In other circumstances, however, birds like magpie, crow, pied wagtail, sparrow and woodpigeon, which all feed on the road, are quite visible from a considerable distance and are killed unnecessarily by drivers who make no concession to the bird by slowing down.

Birds suffer from ailments of one kind or another just as humans do. The illness need not be serious to bring about the bird's death: a sick bird is a slower bird, ill-equipped to evade a predator and probably less likely to survive cold weather or find food in a time of shortage. It is for this reason that the true cause of death is difficult to pinpoint: a slightly unhealthy bird can die of cold just as a bird stunned by a collision may be eaten by a fox, cat or crow.

Other birds die as a result of fighting. Most fights between birds are merely brief skirmishes in which neither contestant suffers anything more than a few ruffled feathers, although occasionally they are more violent. The blackbird seems to indulge in especially vicious battles and sometimes combat results in death or severe injury to one party. Fatal squabbles are most likely to break out in suburban areas where blackbirds are crowded together in dense populations, and would seem to be less common among other species. Even the fiercely aggressive robin uses its red breast and song as threats to avoid coming to blows, though from time to time robins do kill one another.

Birds may die at any time of the year and winter is not necessarily the time of greatest mortality for garden birds.

SURVIVAL RATES

The journey from egg to breeding adult is fraught with danger. In open nests fewer than half the eggs laid produce fledged young. Hole-nesting birds have a much higher success rate in this respect, with young birds successfully fledging from the large majority of eggs laid. Many of these species, however, only raise one brood a year, in Britain, whereas small birds using open nests usually raise two or three broods, or even more in a few species. The net result for the two methods of nesting is therefore probably not dissimilar. There is also the problem of egg-stealing which, fortunately, is less popular as a hobby among young boys than in past years. Although it is illegal, there are still raids on nests, including those of the more common birds which frequent gardens, but not enough to be a major threat. Sadly, the same cannot be said of certain rare species, whose eggs are coveted by the serious collector, often greedy, unscrupulous and wealthy.

Thankfully, it is possible to say that serious egg-collecting is far less common than it was in Victorian times and in the early part of this century and is still declining.

Once out of the nest, young birds face a difficult time. The death rate during the first few days after fledging is higher than at any other time in a bird's life. Populations can vary slightly from year to year and in some years the young birds will survive better than in others, possibly because of the weather or food supply in the winter months. As a general rule, however, the majority of birds which leave the nest in summer are dead by next spring. It has been estimated that only 20–25% of young house sparrows reach maturity, and the survival rates for other garden birds in their first year may be even less.

Many parent birds which manage to fledge their young in fact do not achieve full breeding success, for unless at least one of the offspring joins the breeding stock next year (or at some future date among those birds which do not breed in their first year) breeding cannot be regarded as having been successful. In fact, some broods can be wiped out within a few weeks or even days of having left the nest. Only one-fifth of blackbirds which fledge survive five days and, of those that do, one in five will die before another fortnight has passed.

Most of the smaller birds we see in our gardens have an average life expectancy of between one and two years. Very few small garden birds reach the age of six. The death rate among adult birds, although nowhere near as high as that amongst the first-year birds, may still surprise some readers. The average annual mortality of adult blackbirds is about 33%, of adult house sparrows roughly 40%, and of adult great tits and starlings approximately 50%. The birds which have the lowest annual mortality are mainly the larger birds, such as some gulls with an average mortality of a mere 5%. The swift is an exception among small birds with a low mortality rate of an estimated 20% or lower.

To some people, the thought of all but one of the young blue tits which left the nest-box in the garden being dead by next April is perhaps depressing. In rough terms what normally happens, however, is that one of the two adults and all but one of the young will die, the two surviving birds 'replacing' the two which bred the previous year, thus ensuring a constant population, rather than the over-population which would result if they all survived.

Few birds reach genuine old age in the wild and even fewer, if any, die as a result of senility: a wild bird without all of its faculties is likely to die by some other means. So, because birds, unlike humans and their domestic animals, do not usually reach an age when death becomes more likely, they face a constant and uniform chance of dying throughout their lives after their first year.

SICKNESS, DISEASE AND PARASITES

Wild birds die from countless diseases, bacteria, fungi, injuries, parasites and other ailments, but their ability to overcome what would seem to be quite serious handicaps is frequently surprising. Some manage with only one leg, and probably have a better chance of survival in a garden where supplies of food may be more readily available. One male robin, though lame in one leg, not only lived and bred successfully in a garden for three years but was such a dominant bird that he held the same territory for that time and even bullied other species at the bird-table. In fact, observation suggests that handicapped birds which survive are frequently more aggressive.

In most cases, however, even a minor ailment, especially in times of food shortage or bad weather, is likely to result in death. In sub-zero temperatures, a small bird has a struggle to feed well enough to maintain its body temperature without the added difficulty of an injury or disability, and is unlikely to last for more than half a day without food. In warmer weather, small birds can survive for rather longer without food, and larger birds like owls and other birds of prey can go without food for several days.

Variously afflicted birds are regularly seen at bird-tables. Chaffinches, for instance, seem to be especially prone to a foot deformity which gives them thick legs and an apparent 'club foot'. Observation suggests that males are more likely to suffer from this complaint than females. It is also possible that gregarious species, such as finches, contract more diseases than solitary birds, such as robins, which come into contact with few of their own kind.

Another common ailment is a deformity of the beak. Sometimes one or both mandibles grow so long that the bird is unable to feed. Blue tits, blackbirds and chaffinches are among the species which can suffer in this way. Other birds can suffer the loss of one eye but sometimes survive in spite of this, although flying straight is a problem. They rely on their fellows to help with finding food and to warn of the approach of a predator. One complaint which almost inevitably proves fatal, however, is gape-worm or 'gapes', which causes the victim to hold its beak wide open and take deep, rasping breaths. This incurable disease is familiar to owners of cage-birds, but can afflict many species of wild birds including robins, finches, song and mistle thrushes, redwings and redstarts.

This parasite is one of many which live on or inside birds. Internal parasites or endoparasites include worms, flukes and mites, while lice, fleas, ticks and flies comprise the main external parasites or ectoparasites. The latter, which suck the bird's blood or live on its dead skin or feathers, are rarely fatal. The birds may suffer minor irritation from their external parasites and can remove some of them by preening and bathing. Occasionally the bird's feathers fail to grow properly because of the attentions of parasites, but as long as the flight feathers still perform their intended function and the grey lining feathers are sufficient to provide insulation the bird need not suffer unduly, and new feathers often grow at the next moult. In one instance, a male great tit lacked about one third of his yellow breast feathers for an entire winter.

Of course, external parasites can cause death to weak or badly affected birds and, more especially, to small nestlings. In fact, nests frequently become infested with a rich assortment of spiders, beetles, larvae and fleas. House sparrows' nests which are used throughout the year for roosting as well as breeding purposes are particularly vulnerable. The nests of swifts, swallows and house martins are liable to infestations of the flightless louse-fly. This creature which looks like a fly with virtually no wings occurs on most individuals of these species and sucks their blood. A dozen or more may live on one bird. When the bird is handled, the louse-fly frequently runs out onto the human hand before disappearing again under the bird's feathers. This creature has evolved a life-cycle which takes maximum advantage of its host: the pupae spend the winter months in or near the nests of the birds while the owners are in Africa, and emergence in early summer is timed perfectly to coincide with the hatching of the young birds.

Such a method will only work among species of birds such as the swifts and hirundines which return to the same nests year after year. Many of the garden birds which raise two or more broods in one breeding season even make a new nest each time. This may be to give them the benefit of a clean, parasite-free nest each time; and it has been proved that among hole-nesting species, if they do raise a second brood, there is a higher failure rate when the same hole is re-used.

WEATHER

It is not just in the winter months that bird deaths result from adverse weather conditions. In summer a cold, wet spell may cause young nestlings and even some adult birds to die. Such conditions drastically reduce the number of flying insects; so swallows, house martins and swifts may suddenly find it difficult to obtain food. Migratory birds in spring and autumn can die on passage if they meet cold weather and bad storms. It is not unusual for large numbers to perish in blizzards or to die of exhaustion in gales. When undergoing the physical strain of raising young, possibly involving more than one brood, many adults neglect themselves, lose weight and die before the end of the summer.

Even in prolonged hot weather in summer, ground-feeding birds may suffer severe difficulty. The blackbirds and thrushes, for example, are unable to pierce the concrete-like earth to reach the worms, which have worked their way further below the surface anyway. Woodpigeons, sparrows and finches, too, can find themselves suddenly deprived of food if dry weather permits an early harvest.

Nevertheless, it is the bitter cold of a really severe winter which is the real killer, when well over half the garden birds can die. In the Arctic winter of 1962–3, in some parts of Britain the populations of robin, dunnock, blue tit, great tit and coal tit fell by up to 80%. When the ground is frozen or, worse still covered by deep snow, the ground-feeding birds experience extreme hardship and thousands upon thousands of thrushes, blackbirds and redwings die. The very small birds probably suffer most, and so many goldcrests, long-tailed tits, wrens and treecreepers died in 1962–3 that in some parts of the country whole populations were wiped out and it took many years for the numbers to recover their former levels. Even the green woodpecker suffered huge losses because it relies on ants and ant pupae,

taken from the ground, for much of its diet. The species which fare best at such times are the tree-feeding ones, including most of the finches, and adaptable birds like crows and house sparrows.

If the cold spell is extended over a lengthy period (which is far worse than a short snap, no matter how severe), the strength of the birds is sapped away hour by hour, day by day. In the increasingly desperate search for food, to maintain body temperatures, energy is used up at a greater rate and death is not far away. Many birds die on cold nights. Wrens, even though huddled together in a bundle for warmth, perish, whole groups at a time. Other birds such as

In extremely cold weather, it is the very small birds which are most likely to suffer. In really severe winters, long-tailed tits, for example, may die in large numbers.

starlings, house sparrows and finches sometimes sleep in quite exposed places, on ledges on buildings, in leafless trees, on the tops of tall cranes on building-sites. There have been cases of hundreds of sodden corpses found on the ground below such roosts after a heavy fall of snow, hail or even rain.

In winter, some of the birds which live close to man have a better chance of survival. As well as food which is deliberately put out on bird-tables there is a ready supply of food which is inadvertently provided: discarded scraps and waste-matter at rubbish tips, waste-bins in parks, compost-heaps in gardens; fodder for livestock, pets and other domestic animals; spilt grain in farm-yards; seeds and berries on garden shrubs.

As mentioned earlier, a garden-dwelling bird may benefit in other ways too. The ground temperature can be several degrees higher than in exposed places so the ground may soften or the snow may melt in small pockets around buildings. Walls and fences can often provide shelter from chilling winds, and under bushes, shrubs and deep inside hedges the temperature may be high enough for wrens, dunnocks, blackbirds and thrushes to find enough food for their needs. At night-time, too, the buildings can provide protection: wrens and other birds may sleep in nooks and crannies in walls and even inside sheds and garages.

In cold weather large numbers of birds arrive in Britain, fleeing from the even more severe conditions further north and east. Within the British Isles, there is considerable movement towards the south and west where the weather, in most winters, is milder. The winter of 1962–3 was an exception, however, and thousands of finches, redwings, starlings, song thrushes and other birds found the conditions in the south-west of England even harsher than in those areas from which they had fled. They died because their instinct had led them to a course of action which in another year would have been their salvation. In that winter, those birds, including robins, blackbirds, thrushes, goldfinches and wagtails, which moved south into Europe, some driven to do so late in winter by the cold weather, survived much better.

PREDATORS

For small and medium-sized birds in wooded areas the most dangerous predator is the sparrowhawk. A pair of adult sparrowhawks raising an average brood can account for approximately 2,000 small birds in a year. The greatest threat comes in June and early July when the adult sparrowhawks have their hungry youngsters to feed and when inexperienced, recently-fledged young birds are in abundance, many of which are easy victims for even the most incompetent hunter. Birds the size of a blackbird or larger are relatively safe at this time for, while the young are in the nest, the smaller male sparrowhawk does all the hunting, devoting his attention to birds like tits, robins and sparrows. In his study of tits Christopher Perrins cites an example of a brood of young sparrowhawks being fed 274 birds in 24 days. Of these 213 were tits.

Because this dashing bird of prey is becoming increasingly common in the suburbs of some towns in Britain, more and more garden birds are being taken; on some occasions they are plucked from the bird-table close to the house. This should not be a cause for concern—rather the opposite. The sparrowhawk is a fine bird whose welcome presence lends a garden colour and drama. It is part of the natural scheme of things, and is never going to be so numerous as to pose a threat to the population of any other species.

In fact, this is true of all natural predators: they ensure a correct and healthy balance, often keeping potential pest numbers in check and, where a population is increasing too rapidly for its own good, they ensure that individuals have a quick death rather than a slow, lingering one resulting from food shortage. The tawny owl is a similar example. It survives well in many suburban areas and, now that rodents are less plentiful in many towns, feeds largely on house sparrows and other small birds, feeding its young almost exclusively on them. Often the victims are dislodged from their roosts, even from ivy growing on the side of a building, as the owl drops down from above or strikes it with its wings. Problems only arise when man's activities create an artificial situation in which unnatural

predators thrive: rats, grey squirrels, and, of course, cats. In most towns these replace the foxes, stoats, weasels and sparrowhawks of woodland.

Despite these threats, however, the numbers of most common garden birds remain fairly stable. There are limited territories and nest-sites, with a 'floating' population of surplus birds: the breeding population is more or less constant, in most cases at maximum density. Predated birds are quickly replaced by those that are spare and which would not otherwise be able to establish themselves in a breeding territory. In a limited area, of course, or in one particular garden, the bird population may be adversely affected by particularly efficient cats with strong hunting instincts. In broad terms, though, the local cats, if not too numerous, serve a similar purpose to the natural predators in country districts. Blackbird, wren, dunnock, starling and even the alert house

The kestrel is quite common in many towns, although it tends to hunt in open spaces rather than in gardens. Although small rodents form the bulk of the kestrel's diet, small town-dwelling birds are also taken. The predator which poses by far the greatest threat to birds in towns and gardens, however, is the domestic cat. Some cats are extremely efficient hunters and kill many birds which they do not bother to eat.

sparrow are all common victims, and yet there is no evidence that populations suffer as a result. Robins are also caught, possibly as a result of their extreme tameness, but, unlike the other birds, they are rarely eaten. Though considered a delicacy in France and other European countries, the robin appears to be distasteful to cats. Cats which catch robins possibly do so instinctively or for 'amusement', but are unlikely to make the same mistake twice.

Although rats sometimes kill unwary birds feeding on the ground, they are, like grey squirrels, more of a threat to eggs and small nestlings than to adult birds. Dogs, as the birds well know, are not to be feared.

Birds which feed on the ground are more prone to attack from cats; those that sing and perch on exposed branches are more open to attack by sparrowhawks. Woodpeckers and treecreepers clinging close to a tree trunk are less conspicuous. In addition, with the exception of the green woodpecker, they rarely alight on the ground. When danger threatens, a woodpecker immediately slips round to the other side of the tree, so placing the trunk between itself and the potential attacker. From the safety of this hiding place, it will suspiciously peer round the trunk until the intruder moves away, or fly off if the situation becomes too dangerous. The treecreeper, on the other hand, will usually stay exactly where it is if, for example, a sparrowhawk flies past, but will press itself close to the trunk, thereby concealing the creamy white flanks and underside. The treecreeper's upper parts are mottled brown, which blends beautifully with the bark of the tree. Other birds are able to 'freeze' in a similar way if threatened. A wren has been recorded remaining quite motionless for two and a half minutes. In this way a cat can pass by quite close without noticing the bird. Even if caught, or handled by a human, a wren will sometimes feign death until a lapse in the assailant's concentration permits a sudden escape.

To protect themselves against danger, birds have evolved a variety of alarm calls. In many cases, different species which frequent a particular habitat recognise each other's warning signals and sometimes share a common or similar warning call. Some, including wren, blackbird, house sparrow, great tit, blue tit, long-tailed tit, and some finches, possess one kind of alarm call to indicate a threat by a ground-predator, and a quite different one to warn of an avian attack, sometimes referred to as a 'hawk alarm' call. When one bird gives this call, most of the small birds nearby dive for cover or take defensive measures of some sort. It has been claimed that birds, when giving the 'hawk alarm' call, can 'throw' their voice, like a ventriloquist, in an attempt to confuse the hawk. Many thin, high-pitched bird calls are difficult for the human ear to locate, but this is not necessarily deliberate. A bird of prey relies on vision rather than sound when launching an attack, and anyone who has seen at close hand a sparrowhawk or falcon 'stooping' after prey will be conscious of the single-mindedness of the attack and the unlikelihood of the predator being distracted by a sound.

At any time of the year a hawk or owl is likely to be chased and harried by smaller birds, and a prowling cat sometimes receives the same treatment. However, it is during the nesting season that these 'mobbings' are most intense. As soon as the cat or roosting owl is spotted by one bird the blackbirds begin to 'chink' loudly, chaffinches 'pink', wrens and robins 'tick' violently and the tits chatter angrily; indeed most of the local birds hurl abuse at the intruder in an attempt to drive it off.

The breeding season is, in fact, a dangerous time for birds. As we have seen, the males draw attention to themselves by singing and displaying and later, when the eggs have been laid, the incubating bird, in many cases the female, is literally a sitting target. When feeding young, both parents take risks that they would not contemplate at other times. Furthermore because they make regular flights along the same route to and from the nest they increase the chances of being intercepted by a watchful predator.

Nest Predation

The nests themselves whether containing eggs or young birds attract the attentions of many predators. In woodland, the most serious threat among the mammals is the weasel. Like the stoat, which also takes eggs and nestlings, it can climb well and enter nest-holes, often killing and eating the sitting parent as well as the contents of the nest. When taking young birds, the weasel usually backs out of the nest cavity with one nestling at a time before eating each one in turn outside. There have been cases, however, of a weasel devouring a whole brood inside the nest-hole and then finding itself too bloated to get out again! Grey squirrels also regularly raid nests for eggs and young, sometimes gnawing open the entrance to a hole-nest. Foxes, cats and rodents are all prodigious nest-destroyers.

Among the birds, the corvids present an even bigger threat, flight giving them a better chance of spotting nests. They locate nests either by watching the activities of the parent birds or by systematically scouring bushes and hedges, often returning after a few days to a site they have already raided to take the replacement clutch. Jays are inveterate nest-raiders in woodland but are not common in many gardens. Crows and jackdaws are rather more numerous but are still not a major problem. The real villain is the magpie, a very proficient 'nester' and, unfortunately, very much on the increase in many towns and suburbs. Unlike the case of the sparrowhawk, mentioned earlier, this development is a matter for concern: it is not unknown for a pair of magpies to destroy virtually all the open cup nests in a particular locality.

Against a really determined assault there is very little a small bird can do. The corvids usually wait until the parent bird is away from the nest before carrying out the raid. When the parent returns to find the raid in progress, it will try to lure the assailant away or drive it off, but this is not easy when there is a big difference in size between victim and offender. Some blackbirds can be quite fierce and have been known to strike the head of a human interfering with their nest; and, of course, the tawny owl often attacks humans who approach too near to its nest, and has inflicted serious eye damage on a number of people. For the most part, though, the defending bird has to rely on threat and distraction to defend its eggs and young. An incubating female great tit, for example, will lunge forward towards any object entering the nest-hole, emitting a loud, snake-like hiss. The hollow nest-chamber can lend the noise a grotesque resonance so that it sounds like a snarl.

If the attacker flies off with the nestlings, the unfortunate parents will usually give chase for a short distance, sometimes causing the offender to drop its prize. In such a case, however, the young birds will be left to die on the ground below, for the parents will not pick them up and return them to the nest or attempt to feed them.

Small rodents such as shrews, voles and long-tailed field mice, if they find a clutch of eggs, will nibble a small hole in the shell and drink the contents. Coal tits, whose nests are often in small holes close to the ground among the roots of a tree, and treecreepers are common victims. Great spotted woodpeckers sometimes raid nests in tree-holes and nest-boxes, usually drilling a hole in the outer shell, below the nest-hole entrance, at the level at which the young are to be found inside. To a woodpecker, tiny pink nestlings must look just like fat, oversized grubs.

The level of nest predation is difficult to estimate and undoubtedly varies greatly, depending on the number of potential predators, and other factors such as weather. In some years, for example, the leaf-growth is retarded and birds begin nesting before there is sufficient foliage to provide an acceptable degree of seclusion. In some places, like many suburban gardens, a shortage of good nest-sites, combined with a large population of cats or magpies, may result in a low rate of nesting success. Among those birds which make open nests later clutches have a better chance of survival, probably because of the denser foliage. Ian Newton quotes interesting figures which show that whereas 37% of green-finch nests were predated in April and May only 22% suffered in July and August; similarly, in woodland, 85% of bullfinch nests fell victim to predation in April and May but the figure fell to 30% in July and August.

POISONS

In most cases birds which die as a result of poisoning do so accidentally, unfortunate vic-tims of attempts by farmers, fruit-growers and gardeners to kill pests such as weeds, insects, slugs or rodents or to control crop disease. If a sub-lethal dose is taken, the bird may not die, although breeding success may suffer if the eggs are infertile or deficient in some other way.

The most notorious cases of poisoning in Britain occurred in the 1950s and early 1960s when thousands of birds died. In 1964, once a definite link had been established between the terrible decline in numbers of birds of prey and the indiscriminate use of organochlorine pesti-cides, voluntary restrictions were introduced for some of these chemicals, including aldrin and dieldrin. In 1971, the voluntary ban was ex-tended. Subsequently, the birds which had previ-ously suffered began a recovery which is still continuing today. There is no room for com-placency, however, for at the time of writing there is evidence that some birds of prey still die or fail to breed successfully as a result of con-tinued use of persistent organochlorines.

It is not just birds of prey that are affected by these poisons; many seed-eating birds such as finches, pigeons and rooks die (even the chaffinch which is far less dependent on seeds than other finches, feeding as it does upon caterpillars and insects in the summer). Poisons invariably kill more than is intended. Dangerous seed-dressings and sprays are still sold by agricultural suppliers and gardening shops. Ants, worms, spiders, mol-luscs, leatherjackets and other invertebrates may contain insecticide poisons, so birds which eat these can accumulate lethal doses over a period of time. Deaths of song-thrushes, blackbirds and other ground-feeding birds have been attributed to this.

NEST-BOXES AND NEST-SITES

An amazing number of nest-box designs exist to cater for a surprising range of birds, including swift, swallow, house martin, treecreeper, great spotted woodpecker, jackdaw, tawny owl, red-start, pied and spotted flycatchers, robin, blue tit, great tit, coal tit, marsh tit, as well as several species which would not be expected to nest in anyone's garden.

For A and B, a length of unplaned soft wood (or 'exterior-use' or marine plywood) is required (1260 × 151 × 19 mm), cut as in (2). In A, if the saw is tilted while making the cut between roof and front, the two panels will have a sloping edge which will aid assembly. For B, it is only necessary to plane one end of the roof section to about a 45° angle, so that the roof lies flush with the back.

The pieces are assembled as in (3). A hammer and 18 mm wire nails can be used, but it is better to drill holes for the nails first or to use screws. The roof of A needs to be hinged. Plastic hinges should be used, or a strip of rubber, secured with 12 mm tacks. The lid also needs to be held in place, either by two 'hook and eye' clips or by 2 pairs of staples and 2 lengths of wire. The hole is cut with a drill attachment or a coping saw, at least 25 mm from the roof. In both designs, the exterior should be treated with 2 or 3 coats of wood preservative such as 'Cuprinol' or creosote, well before the breeding season, and a small drainage hole should be drilled in the floor.

The roof (and possibly the back) can be covered with roofing felt (but do not rely on this as a hinge). The metal plate also shown in (1) will deter squirrels and woodpeckers from enlarging the hole.

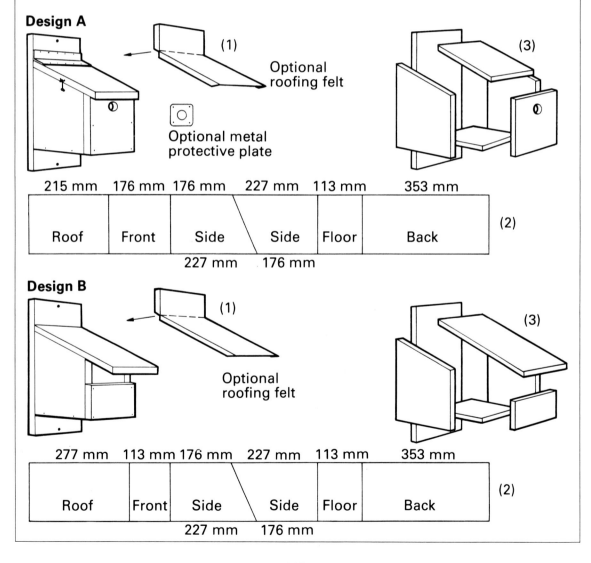

Design A

(1)

Optional roofing felt

Optional metal protective plate

(3)

215 mm	176 mm	176 mm	227 mm	113 mm	353 mm
Roof	Front	Side	Side	Floor	Back

227 mm   176 mm

(2)

Design B

(1)

Optional roofing felt

(3)

277 mm	113 mm	176 mm	227 mm	113 mm	353 mm
Roof	Front	Side	Side	Floor	Back

227 mm   176 mm

(2)

Here only the two most popular types will be described. Details of the more unusual designs are to be found in an excellent little booklet entitled *Nestboxes*, by J. J. M. Flegg and D. E. Glue, which is available from The British Trust for Ornithology (whose address is given in the Appendix). The two conventional nest-boxes, the most appropriate for the majority of gardens, are extremely easy to make; all that is needed is a length of wood, a few nails and some basic tools (*see* page 108).

Design A is used by blue tit, great tit, coal tit, marsh tit, nuthatch, house sparrow, tree sparrow and possibly even wren and treecreeper. In a few privileged, large gardens in certain parts of the country it attracts redstart and pied flycatcher. The size of the hole is important. In most gardens, house sparrows are present and are likely to dominate the nest boxes, unless, that is, the hole is too small to allow them to enter. A hole of 28 mm in diameter is recommended, therefore, through which the other species mentioned can pass but house sparrows cannot. (Redstarts prefer slightly larger holes.)

Design B, the open-fronted type, is used by robin, spotted flycatcher, redstart and occasionally wren and pied wagtail. Nests placed in this type of box are prone to predation, so special care should be taken in the siting of the box.

If you do not wish to attempt the construction yourself, but prefer to buy a nest-box, be warned: some that are on sale in gardening shops and pet shops are not only exorbitantly priced but also badly designed and shoddily made. Many are too small, the hole is often the wrong size, and some appear to serve more as absurd garden ornaments than practical nest-sites for birds. Typical faults include the awful nest-box/bird-table combination and the provision of a perch at the entrance, which serves no purpose whatsoever for the parent birds but permits corvids and starlings to perch while they pluck the young nestlings from the box and devour them. It is far better to purchase a box from the Royal Society for the Protection of Birds (*see* Appendix). The two boxes shown opposite have been adapted, with permission, from an RSPB design.

The reader may wish to design his own box.

The main points to be borne in mind are that the interior should be dry, cool (so metal is not a good idea) and spacious. A family of well-grown blue tits (and it is worth remembering that broods of fifteen or more are not unusual) may suffer in a small nest-box. The floor space, therefore, should measure at least 113×151 mm and the bottom of the entrance hole in type A should be at least 100 mm from the floor.

Probably the most important decision concerning a nest-box, particularly in a garden where cats are a serious threat, is where to site it. The box should be in a sheltered and secluded spot, protected as far as possible from wind, rain and predators, including humans. If it faces west, into the prevailing wind, rain may drive in and soak the interior; and if it faces south, particularly in the case of the open-fronted type, the young birds may suffer discomfort from the heat of the sun. The box should, in any case, be hung tilted marginally forward so that the entrance points very slightly towards the ground, thus providing further protection from rain and direct sunlight.

Nest-boxes should be placed well out of the reach of cats on a wall, or tree trunk, remembering that cats can climb well and can also work their way downwards from a suitable ledge above the nest-box. Holly branches, rose cuttings or other thorny vegetation can be used successfully to keep cats at bay. They can be tied around the nest-box or placed at the base of the tree or post on which the box is positioned. If the box is fairly low to the ground, it should be well away from thick ground cover behind which a cat could lurk in wait for the parent birds as they fly to and from the nest. To ensure that the parent birds have peace and quiet, the site should be well away from human disturbance and, if vandals are a likely threat (and, sadly, this is often a danger) the box should be hidden from view and out of reach well above head height.

The open-fronted variety of nest-box is not as popular with birds as is often supposed, mainly because in exposed places it represents a major security risk. Robins, for example, are extremely secretive when nesting and often ignore these nest-boxes. It is a good idea to place the box, therefore, where there is a screen of vegetation or foliage, perhaps among creepers, ensuring that there are no branches close enough to assist a predator. Robins and spotted flycatchers which use this kind of box often nest close to occupied dwellings, so a box placed in a shed, garage or outhouse which is permanently open, or even on the wall of the house, may be safer from attacks by jays, crows and other predators which are wary of approaching very close to human presence.

It is possible to help the garden birds to nest successfully in many other ways. For example, in April and May, feathers, hair or carpet fluff can be put in the garden. Some species, like great tit and long-tailed tit, will collect such items to line their nests.

Many birds nest in ramshackle sheds and outhouses with permanent gaps through which the birds can enter and leave. If your tool shed or garage has a slight space above a badly fitting door, a loose panel, or a broken window which does not have to be repaired (or better still no doors at all!) you may well be providing nest-sites for blackbird, song thrush, robin, wren and possibly spotted flycatcher. A ledge, preferably high up near the ceiling, may also attract a pair of swallows.

A male pied flycatcher arrives at the entrance of a nest-box with food for its nestlings. This nest-box (design A) has been fitted with a metal plate to prevent squirrels from enlarging the hole and forcing an entry.

If house martins nest under the eaves of the house but suffer from interference by house sparrows, it is worth destroying the martins' nest-cups during the winter months to prevent house sparrows taking them over before the house martins return. They will rebuild the nests when they arrive the following April or May, by which time the house sparrows' nesting programmes will be well advanced elsewhere.

Simply by leaving parts of the garden overgrown, nest-sites can be provided. A thick hedge, perhaps with nettles growing beneath, or a patch of brambles and long grass may be suitable for blackbird, song thrush, wren, robin, willow warbler, chiffchaff, dunnock, blackcap, finches and several other species. Tangles of creepers, such as honeysuckle, possibly growing against a wall, and shrubs with thorns, like hawthorn, attract all these species as well as goldcrest, long-tailed tit and spotted flycatcher. Dense ivy growing up walls and mature trees can provide nest-sites too. Dead trees will be of use to nesting woodpeckers and rotten bark hanging loose from the trunk is ideal for treecreepers. By removing a brick or two from an old garden wall you can create a nest-hole for wrens, pied wagtails, spotted flycatchers or even, in the right area, redstarts.

It is worth remembering that many of these sites, including holes and nest-boxes, can be used as warm roosts. Tawny owls often spend the day hidden in thick ivy, and a wide variety of birds roost in evergreen bushes, hedges and trees. In very cold weather, wrens often sleep in nest-boxes, and sometimes boxes are taken over by hibernating small mammals such as dormice and long-tailed field mice.

NEST ETIQUETTE

If birds nest in your garden, whether in a nest-box or elsewhere, it is a temptation to 'see how they are getting on'. There is a danger, though, that the birds will desert if they have to suffer excessive disturbance. Considerable pleasure can be derived from observing nesting birds without danger to the birds, as long as a few simple rules are followed.

1) Inspect the nest not more than once a day, choosing a time, if possible, when both parents are away, rather than driving off a sitting bird. If the parents return before you have completed your inspection, they will possibly give their alarm calls. When you have completed your inspection, which should not take more than a few minutes at the most, they will continue their activities.

2) Do not disturb the birds late in the day. If a parent is alarmed shortly before dusk and does not return to the nest that night, the eggs will chill or young nestlings will die of cold.

3) Tits, nuthatches and one or two other species bury their eggs underneath nest materials so that they are completely hidden. Be careful not to damage them when inspecting. Similarly, take care when opening the lid of a nest-box which is being used by a pair of nuthatches. These birds usually clog up the cracks around the lid with mud. As the lid is opened, lumps of hard, caked mud may fall onto the eggs or chicks.

4) It is easy to forget that the nest is there. Parent birds should be able to make repeated and regular unhindered journeys to and from the nest. Even robins and blackbirds which were tame in winter can be extremely timid when they have eggs or young in the nest and may be kept away for too long by children playing, someone gardening or just sitting in a deck chair close to the nest. Noisy machinery, such as an electric or motor-driven lawn mower, can cause excessive disturbance. If, by undertaking such activity, you are obviously preventing the birds from feeding young, it is a good idea to work in short bursts, permitting the birds to visit the nestlings in your absence and to make up for lost time. Young nestlings of small birds grow very fast and need all the food their parents can bring them. If they go without food for even a few hours, they can weaken and may die. Parent birds can be kept away from the nest by the sudden appearance close by of a strange object such as washing flapping in the wind or a car.

A nest-box should be big enough to accommodate a large brood of well-grown nestlings. Here fifteen young blue tits have virtually outgrown their nest-box.

5) It is important not to leave a nest-site exposed after inspecting it. Simply part the vegetation and cover it up again when you have finished. Nests which are not well concealed soon fall victim to jays, magpies, cats and other predators. So, too, when trimming a hedge in summer, it is necessary to check that no nest is going to be exposed.

6) Extreme care has to be exercised when the young in the nest are well advanced and the time for their fledging is approaching. The close approach of a human may cause them to 'explode' from the nest before they are really ready, and when their chances of survival are slim. It is better to resist the temptation to inspect a nest which has reached this stage.

7) Many young birds leave the nest of their own accord before they can fly properly. The well-intentioned human, finding a non-flying chick, may think that it has been deserted. Such is rarely the case, so the bird should be left where it is or placed somewhere nearby off the ground in cover. When the parent

returns, the young bird will reveal its presence by calling. Young fledglings should not be taken away to be fed, even for a short period. Wild birds usually die in captivity; unless a bird is obviously injured and unable to fend for itself, it should be left alone.

PROVIDING FOOD

Much has been written in recent years about bird-tables and the food that can be provided for wild birds. It is not necessary here to repeat in detail all the good advice that is available elsewhere, but the more important points are summarised as follows.

Almost any 'human' food can be put out on the bird-table, including cheeses, fat, bacon rind (which should be cut up into small pieces so that the birds will not choke on it), stale cake, biscuits, cooked potato, breakfast cereal, oats, cooked rice, fresh coconut, uncooked pastry, raisins, sultanas and other fruit. Dog and cat food can also be used. Any item which may swell up when wet inside a bird's stomach (e.g. desiccated coconut) should not be used; bread should be soaked first for this reason.

If special bird food is to be purchased the best buys are peanuts, suet, fishermen's maggots, mealworms (which can be bred in a mealworm culture), and sunflower seeds. Peanuts are on sale at many pet shops and greengrocers, and when placed in the familiar hanging basket will attract house sparrow, greenfinch, blue tit, great tit, coal tit, marsh tit, nuthatch, siskin and great spotted woodpecker. Other birds which have been known to try feeding in this way include chaffinch, brambling, redpoll, starling and long-tailed tit. Birds which cannot hang on to the nut-holder will eat the bits that fall onto the

In gardens in wooded suburbs (or if there is a park or a wood nearby), a bag of peanuts will attract several species such as great spotted woodpecker and nuthatch (shown here), as well as the more familiar tits, greenfinches and house sparrows.

ground beneath the bird-table. Salted peanuts should never be used, nor should any salted foods.

Suet is much more difficult to obtain than peanuts. This is not the packeted shredded suet, but chunks straight from the carcass. Few butchers supply it because of EEC arrangements, but some may be able to provide a regular supply. Suet wedged into a log (which can either stand upright in a flower pot or bucket or be suspended from the branch of a tree) will attract great spotted woodpecker, nuthatch, tits and possibly treecreeper. Other birds such as robin and blackbird will also tuck in if they can obtain a secure

hold. Other items which will be well received are mixed wild bird seed, canary seed, chopped hazel and brazil nuts, beech mast and acorns.

When putting food out at the bird-table, there are a few points to be borne in mind. Some of this food should be spread on the ground for ground-feeding birds, such as dunnock, song thrush, redwing and fieldfare, and if snow covers the ground a space should be cleared to help them to find the food. Also, there are some birds which cannot crunch or break open hard seeds and nuts. Although tits can chip away at a peanut or sunflower seed and greenfinches can crunch them, dunnock, robin, long-tailed tit, thrushes and even chaffinches cannot cope with them. It is a good idea, therefore, to chop up nuts and seeds, as well as biscuits, and crispbreads, or break them up in a kitchen grinder. A finely crumbled mixture like this will prove popular with such birds, particularly long-tailed tits. There are few more rewarding sights in the garden than a dozen or more

A greenfinch at a bird-table eating maize. The greenfinch's powerful bill enables it to crunch large, hard nuts and seeds. For some of the other visitors to a bird-table, however, crumbled-up food must be provided.

long-tailed tits swarming all over the bird-table.

Another important consideration is the siting of the bird-table. It should be well away from thick ground cover which could conceal a cat with designs on the birds. However, there should be a tall bush or shrubs a few feet away to permit birds an inconspicuous approach and somewhere to which they can beat a hasty retreat if a sparrowhawk comes dashing through the garden. To avoid the risk of disease, as droppings accumulate, the table should be moved a few feet every few weeks and the top scrubbed clean.

Once a bird-table is set up, it is necessary to maintain a consistent supply of food throughout the winter. Some birds fly considerable distances to garden bird-tables, possibly from local parks or copses. Futile journeys to a table where there is no food mean wasted time and energy; in cold weather, they can spare neither, for not only is food hard to come by but there is also less time to find it. If the food disappears during the first half of the day, the stocks should, if possible, be replenished in the afternoon so that birds can feed well before nightfall. This is particularly important in cold weather when additional energy reserves are required to maintain body temperature at night.

Starlings and sparrows are a problem at some bird-tables, dominating the food supply and chasing off smaller birds. By wrapping thick polythene around the outside of the peanut holder so that only the bottom is uncovered, you can limit the sparrows' activities: the tits can hang on upside-down quite easily. Bird pudding is also a good idea. Various scraps and chopped-up nuts are placed in melted fat in a plastic container (a yoghurt cup, for instance) or half a coconut. As the fat cools and congeals, a solid 'pudding' is formed which can then be hung upside down so that the tits and nuthatches have a distinct advantage over the starlings and sparrows. You may also find that a supply of food very close to the house, even on a window sill, is eaten by robins and blackbirds but ignored by starlings which are rather more wary of humans.

Food should under no circumstances be put out for birds between mid-April and the end of August, the period when parent birds are feeding their young. In spring and summer there are plenty of natural foods anyway (insects, caterpillars and seeds), and if young birds are fed unnatural foods like peanuts, bread or fat they will be unable to digest it and may well die as a result. If the local greengrocer sells bags of peanuts during the summer months, it may well be just because he is unaware of the danger.

As well as a bird-table, another way of providing food for wild birds is to cultivate plants which either attract insects or which produce seeds or fruit that can be eaten by birds. Apple, crab-apple and pear provide food, in the form of rotten windfalls, for blackbirds, thrushes, redwings, fieldfares, blackcaps, marsh tits and even green woodpeckers. Berries of many plants are favoured by different species. Holly, yew, cotoneaster, elder, hawthorn, rowan and blackthorn (sloes) are popular with all five garden thrushes and the first three in that list also attract blackcaps. Pyracantha (firethorn), berberis, mistletoe, buckthorn, blackberry and honeysuckle are also eaten by certain thrushes and blackcaps. Of course, there are other birds which have a taste for these plants. Bullfinches eat the seeds within the berries of pyracantha, rowan and blackberry, and robin, starling, marsh tit, greenfinch and whitethroat will feed on their own personal favourites. The exotic waxwing may be persuaded to enter a garden by rowan, pyracantha or cotoneaster berries in one of those rare 'waxwing winters'. Other bushes and shrubs which may be grown for the birds include ivy, privet, briar rose and snowberry, although the number of species which feed on these is smaller, and they may serve only as a 'last resort' when other food supplies are running short.

It is worth collecting some of these berries in the autumn and keeping them in a freezer until the cold weather. Birds will appreciate them at a time when food is scarce.

In a large garden, another idea is to allow an area to become wild and overgrown. Brambles and nettles attract insects (as do certain shrubs such as veronica and buddleia) and may also offer many potential nest-sites, which could attract some new species to the garden. A very weedy patch provides seeds for finches, dunnocks

115

A mature, wooded garden like this one can provide for the needs of many birds. Flowers, shrubs and fruit bushes provide seeds and berries. Thick hedges and evergreens provide sheltered day-time or night-time roosts as well as nest-sites for dunnocks, thrushes and finches.

and sparrows. Chickweed, thistles, teasel and groundsel, for example, are very much to the liking of goldfinches and other finches. Other weeds which provide food for seed-eating birds include nettle, dock, dandelion, charlock, colts-foot, cranesbill, fumitory, willowherbs, fat hen, knapweed, burdock and various grasses.

Of course, weeds in a garden are anathema to some people. Nevertheless there are many attractive flowers, the seeds of which attract finches and other seed-eaters; aster, cosmos, michaelmas daisy, campanula, petunia, phlox, marigold, sweet william, sunflower and zinnia are some.

Trees, too, are valuable suppliers of seeds. Beech mast is beloved of great tit, nuthatch, chaffinch and brambling, while silver birch, alder and willow appeal to siskins, redpolls and tits. Hazel nuts are broken open and devoured by woodpeckers and nuthatches and ash keys are eaten by several species.

These trees also harbour vast resources of insect life. Oak, willow and silver birch are especially important in this respect, particularly in May and June when a good supply of caterpillars is required for young birds. Dead timber also offers a rich harvest of grubs and insects to woodpeckers and treecreepers. Like many of the living trees, they can provide valuable nest-sites.

Finally, it is necessary to mention water, which is almost as important as food, especially in winter and in times of drought. Any shallow container can serve as a bird-bath as long as the sides are not steep or slippery. If small birds cannot stand in it easily, a stone or a branch should be provided as a perch. In winter, if the water freezes, the ice should be broken or, if possible, the water should be kept above freezing point with an electric pond-heater which can be purchased at many garden centres. Artificial substances such as antifreeze or salt should not be used on any account because the birds' plumage could suffer irreparable damage, and in winter inefficient plumage probably means death.

Even better than a bird-bath is a pond, with gently sloping sides for the birds to use for drinking and bathing. A pond has the added advantage of providing an attractive feature in the garden, rich insect life, such as dragonflies and possibly other creatures like frogs, newts and many other aquatic creatures.

BIRD PROTECTION

Gardens constitute the largest nature reserve in the United Kingdom and every gardener is, in a small way, a warden of his own reserve. It is his responsibility to protect those birds which visit his garden, especially if they have been attracted there by the provision of food and nest-sites.

Cats have been mentioned many times already and they will always pose a threat. Probably the best way of keeping other people's cats out of your garden is to own a dog. However, if a cat owner wants to be a bird gardener, he needs to ensure that all nest-boxes and bird food supplies are well away from danger. For example, the bird-table can be hung from a branch, strong wire or a bracket fixed to a wall. However, the owner should be mindful of the fact that some of the food will end up on the ground beneath and attract ground-feeding birds, so it still needs to be well away from low cover which the cat may use for concealment. Another idea is to hang a bell round the cat's neck; it is reputed to make a cat such an inefficient hunter that he loses interest in the hobby, although there is no proof of this.

It is especially important that fruit cages are completely bird-proof for the good of the birds as well as the raspberries, blackcurrants or strawberries! If the fruit patch is checked twice a day, around midday and again in the evening, any birds which have become trapped will be found and can then be freed. It is also a good idea to tension the netting so that birds which attempt to force an entry do not become entangled in it and die.

Windows are potential killers, too, particularly in spring and summer when adult birds are preoccupied with feeding, young and inexperienced birds are plentiful and the brighter light creates clearer reflections in windows. There are many ways of combating this problem. Probably the best way is to place some conspicuous object just inside the window or to install net curtains, a roller blind or venetian blinds. Alternatively something can be placed on the window panes, such as a colourful floral design, or trellis work and climbing plants can be grown up outside the window, though this will probably cut out too much light. Another possibility is to trail string with ribbons or pieces of cloth attached across the outside of the offending window or to hang strips of plastic, such as are used in hot weather

Starlings, sporting their spotted winter plumage, make use of a bird bath. Most birds drink by scooping water into the beak and then tipping the head back so that the water runs down the throat, as the bird on the right is doing. In winter it is important to provide water for birds as well as food, particularly in freezing conditions.

as a screen to exclude flies. Yet another success-ful method involves placing a cut-out silhouette of a sparrowhawk or an owl on the window pane or placing an imitation bird of prey on the window sill.

Just as the gardener understandably wants to protect his fruit from marauding blackbirds and thrushes so, too, it is to be expected that he will want to protect his other plants from various pests. The indiscriminate use of chemicals in the garden, however, can have serious consequences for birds and other creatures, including insects, some of which are of considerable value to the gardener. It is necessary to exercise caution when using any kind of pesticide, especially when spraying. If water becomes contaminated, birds may be poisoned and pond life will die and, if spraying is carried out when plants are in flower, bees and other useful insects will be killed. Also, of course, by killing off insects the gardener is removing the food supply for insectivorous birds and many weeds produce seeds which finches and other species eat.

Poisoned bait should never be left where birds can find it. Slug pellets should be placed under a board or a plastic container like an old washing up bowl, raised slightly off the ground by a stone so that the slugs can pass underneath. Even if this precaution is taken, birds can still find and eat slugs which contain poison so a better way of killing slugs is to place a plastic pot in the ground and fill it with sugary liquid: the slugs are at-tracted to it but cannot get out. The previous night's 'catch' can be disposed of safely in the morning. Similarly, poison for rats and mice should be placed where only the rodents will find it and not where birds feed. So, too, spring mouse traps should not be used outdoors where innocent birds or other creatures may be caught.

The majority of readily-available garden chemicals are relatively safe to use. At all times, however, the user should follow the instructions carefully and, if in doubt, err on the side of caution and seek advice from a body such as the RSPB, who publish a very helpful booklet entitled *Pesticides and the Gardener*.

On the wider subject of conservation of birds outside the garden, there are several organisa-tions which do valuable work. Their addresses are given in the Appendix.

CHAPTER 6

IDENTIFYING THE BIRDS

The following is a brief description of the majority of birds which are mentioned in this book. It should be pointed out, however, that some of the species included here only occasionally appear in gardens in Britain. Perhaps they just pay fleeting visits on migration or frequent only the larger gardens in the more wooded suburbs or are seen in a few gardens in certain parts of the country.

Of course, it must be stressed that, in extreme circumstances, literally any bird may be found in a garden: rare migrants many miles off course and weakened by a long flight; sea birds blown inland by strength-sapping storms; sick, weak or confused birds of almost any species. So, too, a garden bordering a particular habitat may seem to birds and other creatures merely an extension of that habitat. Thus a garden bordering water meadows or bounded by a river may be suitable for waterside birds over and above those listed. Or a garden overlooking farmland may be visited by yellowhammer or skylark, particularly if grain is scattered on the ground beneath the bird-table. Such a supply of food in the right area, possibly adjacent to rural woodland, may well persuade pheasants to come high-stepping across the lawn. Linnets, too, sometimes enter country gardens and are not infrequently recorded in towns, usually feeding on weeds on derelict, overgrown industrial sites. Also, during migration, almost any bird can pay a surprise visit to a garden. For instance, in late summer, soft fruits sometimes attract warblers. So, too, an alert ornithologist may record a wide variety of birds overflying almost any garden which could be added to the list of garden or town birds.

Rigid divisions or distinctions are inevitably arbitrary and probably of dubious value. The question is asked again: what *is* a garden bird? The list of birds which *might* visit a garden is almost endless. That it is so is both unsurprising and gratifying, for it thereby reflects the marvellous variety and adaptability of the natural world in general and birds in particular.

The species are arranged roughly according to size, starting with the smallest, but because they are also placed together in family groups (within which there can be considerable variations of size), this is not completely consistent throughout. For photographs of those species not illustrated here, refer to the index.

GOLDCREST *Regulus regulus*

SIZE   90 mm—the tiniest British bird.

STATUS AND DISTRIBUTION   Very common, throughout the year, anywhere in Britain where there are trees, especially conifers.

IN GARDENS   In summer not frequent unless close to pines, yew, cedar or other conifers. In winter quite common, often accompanying feeding parties of tits. Very rarely visits bird-tables.

Many mistakenly regard the wren as the smallest bird in Britain but the goldcrest is, in fact, smaller. By comparison, even a blue tit, which may be over twice the weight of a goldcrest, can look quite bulky.

With a short tail, making it look almost spherical, this bird is a pale greenish puff-ball. It is not always easy to see the gold crest (actually a yellow stripe on the crown rather than a raised crest) unless the bird is excited or agitated when the crown feathers are fluffed up slightly. The female's stripe is yellow, the male's yellow mixed with orange. More noticeable than the crest are the creamy wing bars. The tiny straight beak is even slimmer than the pine needles from which much of the bird's insect food is taken.

Often the first clue to the proximity of some goldcrests is the whispy, high-pitched call, suggestive of some constantly turning machinery in need of oil. The sound is so thin that the human ear may find it difficult to locate the direction from which it comes, and the bird's habit of flitting infuriatingly from one high branch to another often makes it necessary to identify the bird on sound alone. Even so the really patient observer will be richly rewarded, for goldcrests are quite unconcerned by the presence of man. If the birds drop down to lower branches they may continue feeding very close to the observer, almost at times perching on his head!

The goldcrest can match the tits for acrobatics on the slimmest of branches. A familiar feature of its feeding is a brief hover below a branch as insects are picked from the underside of the foliage. In forestry pine plantations, which are usually almost devoid of bird life, the goldcrest is one of the handful of species to be seen regularly.

WREN *Troglodytes troglodytes*

SIZE   95 mm.

STATUS AND DISTRIBUTION   Very common throughout Britain at all times of the year.

IN GARDENS   Common except in very built-up areas. Very occasionally uses nest-boxes.

The wren is possibly the commonest and most widespread bird in the British isles. This may be surprising until one realises that it is able to survive and breed in almost any kind of habitat: towns, parks, gardens, orchards, woods, farmland, as well as moorland and mountains, sea cliffs and open heathland. All it requires is a little low cover: even a thin layer of heather will suffice.

Although many people are vaguely aware of the wren's presence in their gardens, few are truly familiar with its features for it is an independent bird, rarely visiting bird-tables, even in winter when natural food is scarce. From its low whirring flight one has merely an impression of a small brown bullet. A further hindrance to observation is its skulking habit; it spends considerable time hidden from view in deep cover under bushes and shrubs foraging for insects and spiders (its scientific name *Troglodytes* means literally 'cave-dweller').

A good sighting will reveal a stubby bird with pale underparts, russet brown upperparts, a pale stripe above the eye and a short brown tail which is almost permanently cocked stiffly up. Along the edge of the wing, the dark bars on the flight feathers are an attractive feature.

The wren is happy to live very close to man without paying him much attention, displaying indifference rather than tameness. If wrens keep to the bottom of your garden, this probably reflects the arrangement of the garden rather than any shyness on the part of the bird. Any overgrown area, which would be inviting to the wren, is likely to be at a distance from the house. The wren's confiding nature will become apparent in the breeding season when this species regularly nests very close to human activity, in garages, garden sheds and even in the structure of an occupied house.

The wren's song is incredibly loud for the bird's tiny size, with the greatest volume relative to body size of any British song bird. The sight of a cock wren in full song is an extraordinary sight —the entire body is aquiver, the tail cocked and vibrating, head thrown back. The song is delivered with such intensity that the bird appears to be clinging on to the perch so as not to throw itself completely off-balance.

BLUE TIT *Parus caeruleus*

SIZE   115 mm.
STATUS AND DISTRIBUTION   Year-round resident in all parts of Britain except some Scottish islands. Very common.
IN GARDENS   Extremely common. A regular at bird-tables. Uses nest-boxes.

The blue tit is the archetypal tit, flitting and darting, apparently never still, now hanging from the peanuts, now chittering angrily at another bird, now diving away to the garden hedge with some food in its beak.

Its appearance is very familiar, although it is often confused with the great tit. The crown is azure blue (black in the great tit), its wings are blue or blue-green (the great tit's are blue-grey), the chest only shows the faintest suggestion of a black stripe (unlike the great tit which has a strong prominent stripe). The blue tit has a dark line through the eye and is considerably smaller than the great tit. The two sexes are very similar and often identical to the human eye though in the breeding season some males look extremely bright with azure-blue markings. This is not a foolproof way of telling them apart, though, because the brightness of the plumage can vary in individual birds.

The blue tit can be found anywhere where there are trees, scrub, bushes or hedges. In autumn and winter it can be found searching for insects in reed beds. Basically it is insectivorous but one of the reasons for the success of this species is its adaptability, feeding on a wide variety of other things such as nuts, buds, seeds and almost any scrap left out on a bird-table. Furthermore, it is a determined little character.

At a bird-table crowded with birds it is rarely the blue tit which is chased off by other species. If it is dislodged by a surprise attack, it is soon back diving at the intruder, even a bigger bird such as a greenfinch or great tit, to harry and hustle it away from the food. At such times the blue crest is raised as part of the threat.

The blue tit has a considerable variety of calls and chattering bursts. In the breeding season, the male has a brief, chirpy song which includes some of its familiar calls and trills.

GREAT TIT *Parus major*

SIZE   140 mm—the size of a robin.
STATUS AND DISTRIBUTION   Year-round resident in all parts of Britain except some Scottish islands. Very common.
IN GARDENS   Extremely common. A regular at bird-tables. Uses nest-boxes.

The great tit has a black head, except for the white triangular cheeks, and a black throat which extends down the centre of the yellow chest in a bold, black stripe. The sheen on the black crown can cause it to look blue-black in certain lights. The tail is longer than the blue tit's and looks dark grey with white outer feathers which are quite prominent as the bird flies away. The back is a rich olive-green, the wings blue-grey.

The sexes are similar but it is possible to tell them apart. The cock has bolder markings: a blacker, glossier head and the black stripe down the chest and belly is much broader, especially between the legs.

In its feeding habits the great tit has similar tastes to the blue tit, feeding on various insects, buds, seeds and nuts. It has a stronger beak than its smaller relative enabling it to break open quite hard items of food. Its noisy attacks on nuts, which are often pinned to the branch by the foot, can sound like the tapping of a woodpecker.

Great tits are as agile and acrobatic as blue tits but, when feeding in trees, the heavier great tit cannot suspend itself from very slender twigs and spends more time foraging for food on the ground. In autumn it often joins chaffinches and nuthatches searching among the fallen leaves.

Like all tits, the great tit has a range of chittering calls, usually distinguished from the blue tit's by being deeper and louder. The male's song (a feature of early spring days) consists of a repetition of two notes which sound like 'teacher, teacher', 'see-saw, see-saw', or 'ox-eye, ox-eye', the latter being its nickname in some districts.

COAL TIT *Parus ater*

SIZE 115 mm—the same size as a blue tit.
STATUS AND DISTRIBUTION Common, year-round resident throughout Britain where there are trees.
IN GARDENS Regularly visits gardens and bird-tables. Uses nest-boxes.

The coal tit's crown is glossy black, the cheeks white and there is quite a large black bib which, with the white patch on the back of the head, is the easiest way of distinguishing this bird from the two other similarly coloured tits, the marsh tit and willow tit. The chest is creamy buff with no central stripe; the upperparts are grey.

The bird's natural food is similar to that of the blue tit and the great tit, mainly a variety of insects, buds and seeds; but unlike them it favours coniferous woodland, where it eats the

The coal tit (above) is a regular at many bird-tables. The marsh tit (below left) is not uncommon in well-wooded suburbs, but the willow tit (below) is only a rare visitor to a few gardens.

seeds from fir-cones. In fact, apart from the gold-crest with which it often mixes, the coal tit is just about the only small bird seen regularly in some forestry plantations.

Like all the tits it has a variety of trills and calls, some of which resemble the high-pitched sounds of the goldcrest. Its song is quite distinctive, sounding like 'sittoo, sittoo, sittoo' or 'too, wittoo, wittoo', the sound being repeated four or five times in each refrain at greater speed than the great tit's 'ox-eye, ox-eye'.

When visiting gardens it can become even bolder than the other tits, allowing humans to approach within arm's length. Over a period of time, it is possible to persuade this species to take food from the hand like a robin. It is similarly fearless of any larger birds which may attempt to drive it away from the bird-table, cheekily continuing to feed on one side of the nutholder while a great tit or greenfinch threatens from the other side. In fact, it is small enough to enter some nut-baskets through the gap at the top, helping itself to whole nuts at each visit while the bigger birds hang on the outside laboriously extracting small chippings.

MARSH TIT *Parus palustris*

SIZE   115 mm—the same size as a blue tit.
STATUS AND DISTRIBUTION   Year-round resident throughout England, Wales and some parts of southern Scotland. Quite common in mature deciduous woodland. In spite of its name, not a marshland bird.
IN GARDENS   Not as numerous as blue, great and coal tits but regularly visits gardens and bird-tables. Uses nest-boxes but does so less readily than previous three tits.

Although not as colourful as some tits, the marsh tit is an extremely neat and trim bird. Its well-defined black cap, pale cheeks, uniform grey-brown back and creamy buff underparts give the marsh tit a smart, dapper appearance. It is some-times confused with the coal tit but this bird lacks the bold, white patch which the coal tit has on the back of its head and the bib under the beak is very small on the marsh tit, whereas the coal

tit's large bib spreads down onto the breast. Confusion is more likely with the almost identical willow tit (*Parus montanus*), but this latter bird is hardly ever seen in gardens. The marsh tit's glossier cap and less heavy-headed build may aid identification but its unmistakable 'pitchoo-pitchoo' call is the most helpful sign.

This species is as willing to visit bird-tables as its better-known relatives and shows all the familiar tit-like characteristics when feeding on a peanut holder. Indeed, it can become so fond of peanuts that it is reluctant to leave them even when a human approaches. One individual became so tame that it would approach to within less than two metres of a human to take peanuts thrown for it onto the ground.

This member of the tit family is rather more reluctant to move far from well-wooded parks and woods so a visit to a garden is less likely if there are few mature trees in the vicinity.

LONG-TAILED TIT *Aegithalos caudatus*

SIZE   140 mm—including a 75 mm tail.
STATUS AND DISTRIBUTION   Common, year-round resident anywhere in Britain where there are trees, bushes or hedgerows.
IN GARDENS   Infrequent and sporadic in most gardens. In cold weather, gardens near wooded areas or parks may be visited frequently. Never uses nest-boxes but visits bird-tables.

A feather-light ball of fluff, the long-tailed tit is a most appealing bird. Its underparts are creamy-white flushed with pink around the flanks, the back and wings a patchwork of black, white, pink and rusty-brown. Black stripes over the eye enclose a white crown. Notice especially the eye-ring, which can be yellow, orange or red. The sexes are alike.

The long-tailed tit's diet consists of small insects, caterpillars, buds and seeds. By comparison with the other tits, to whom it is only partly related, the long-tailed tit has a small, rather weak beak, which may explain why it rarely attempts to feed on the peanuts at the bird-table.

The long-tailed tit does not have a song but its calls are quite distinctive: a harsh little rattle or churr, such as a human might make by lightly vibrating the tongue against the roof of the mouth, and a 'tack' sound as if someone is 'tutting' in annoyance.

Apart from the nesting period (late March–May) birds of this species are permanently together in quite large flocks of about 10 to 20, so if one visits a bird-table then probably the others will too. These flocks are never tightly packed but work their way through the trees in twos and threes, calling to one another repeatedly. Someone familiar with the calls of this species will often be aware of the presence of a party of the birds before they are visible.

This tit is only distantly related to those above which belong to the Paridae family. The main difference is that, though the *Parus* tits always nest in holes, the long-tailed tit builds a domed nest. This most marvellous creation, a neat ball consisting of vast quantities of lichen, moss and cobwebs lined with hundreds, sometimes thousands, of feathers, is unmatched by any other British bird for complexity and beauty.

TREECREEPER *Certhia familiaris*

SIZE   125 mm—slightly smaller than a robin.
STATUS AND DISTRIBUTION   Year-round resident anywhere in Britain where there are trees.
IN GARDENS   An occasional visitor to well-timbered gardens or gardens near wooded areas or parks. More likely to visit a garden in winter, probably with a feeding party of tits. May visit a bird-table. Uses specially designed nest-boxes.

Fundamentally a woodland bird, the treecreeper is perfectly designed for the life it leads. It has creamy white underparts, but by its habit of clinging to the sides of trees the bird presents its back to the viewer. The brown mottled feathers on its back and wings are a marvellous camouflage, looking so much like gnarled bark that the bird is very difficult to see when it remains motionless. Its fine, delicately-curved beak is an ideal tool for winkling out insects from crevices in old bark. Finally, its tail is stiff and strong like a woodpecker's, serving as an extra prop when perched upright on a tree trunk. The sexes are alike. The

Treecreepers are often found in suburbs and gardens with mature trees, and sometimes visit bird-tables.

calls and song are thin, high-pitched, whispy sounds often difficult to locate.

The method of foraging for food is quite distinctive: a treecreeper scuttles up a tree like a mouse, spiralling round the trunk as it climbs; when the top is reached, the bird flies down to the base of another tree and the process is repeated. Not infrequently when a lateral branch is reached the treecreeper continues outwards along the branch still describing a spiral, as much at ease upside down as the right way up. Unlike the nuthatch, the treecreeper does not descend head-first. If it wishes to return to a lower point, it either drops down in its light, flitting flight, or works its way down tail-first.

This species shows little fear of man and the

quiet watcher can be rewarded with extremely close views. One pair of treecreepers continued feeding their young brood with two people only a few paces away and there have been cases of young treecreepers climbing up a motionless human being as if he were a tree.

NUTHATCH *Sitta europaea*

SIZE   140 mm–the same size as a robin.
STATUS AND DISTRIBUTION   A common all-year resident in the southern half of England and Wales. Less common in northern England; absent from Scotland and Ireland. Requires plenty of mature deciduous trees, particularly oak or beech.
IN GARDENS   Quite common in gardens in well-timbered suburban areas or near parks with mature trees. Readily visits bird-tables. Uses nest-boxes.

The nuthatch brings a splash of colour to any garden. The crown, back, wings and tail are an attractive pastel blue, while the chest and flanks are a creamy orange–the flanks being a rich, rusty brown on some males. The design is superbly finished off with a bold black stripe which extends from the beak, through the eye and down the side of the head. It has a stocky, barrel-like appearance.

There are some who resent this bird's presence at their bird-table. Some nuthatches are quite pugnacious and can begin to dominate a bird-table or peanut holder since few small birds would risk a blow from such a powerful bill.

The nuthatch sometimes seems determined to draw attention to itself wherever it is. Its high-pitched 'whit-whit, whit-whit', can carry a surprisingly long distance and its song, 'pee-pee-pee' sounds not unlike a boy whistling his dog. It is a noisy eater, too, frequently hammering loudly on a branch, or a nut which it is trying to crack open.

Such behaviour may suggest that the nuthatch is a kind of woodpecker but it is unlike woodpeckers in several ways: it does not excavate its own nest-hole, it lacks a woodpecker's long tongue and it never uses its tail when in the upright position. It has large, powerful feet which enable it to make its characteristic effortless descent head-first down tree-trunks. The peculiar manner of cocking its head to look and listen for danger is very typical of this bird, although it is not permanently thus as may be suggested by the numerous paintings of the bird in that pose.

CHIFFCHAFF *Phylloscopus collybita* and WILLOW WARBLER *Phylloscopus trochilus*

SIZE   110 mm–fractionally smaller than a blue tit.
STATUS AND DISTRIBUTION   Common throughout Britain in summer but the chiffchaff is absent from most of northern Scotland. Willow warbler much more numerous. In winter a few chiffchaffs remain in Ireland and southern England.
IN GARDENS   In winter–chiffchaffs occasionally; willow warblers never. In spring and autumn–both birds not uncommon, passing through on migration. In summer–willow warbler more likely to breed in or near gardens; in late summer both species may roam gardens with feeding parties of tits. Chiffchaff much less common near build-up areas.

These two delicate warblers are taken together because they are closely related and look almost identical. Both are rather dull, olive- or greenish-yellow birds with pale underparts and a faint yellowy or creamy eyestripe which is not always easy to see.

There are only two ways of making a positive distinction between the two species. One is to hold the bird in the hand and measure the wing feathers, a method invaluable to ringers but of little help to the average garden birdwatcher. The second method is by song. The chiffchaff's song is a repetitive 'chiff-chaff, chiff-chaff', from which it earns its name. In fact the sound is more like 'sip-sap, sip-sap', sometimes reversed to 'sap-sip, sap-sip', often with an odd little scratching, croaky sound interspersed with the main notes, as if the bird is rewinding the mechanism. The willow warbler's song, once learnt, is unmistakable. It is a haunting, rather sad ripple of notes which tumble down the musical scale, the only British birdsong to have such a falling cadence.

It is a sound which can be heard in April, May and June in almost every wooded area in Britain, in parks, copses and many gardens. Both birds can continue singing for hours at a time but because of the monotonous nature of the chiffchaff's song it can soon pall, whereas the willow warbler's song is much more pleasant to the human ear—even when uttered for, apparently, the thousandth time.

In the breeding season, the chiffchaff is far less numerous in Britain than the willow warbler, which is among the most common breeding birds in British woodland. Instead of gardens and suburban parks, the chiffchaff prefers to nest in undergrowth on the margins of woods, or in scrub and belts of trees in open country. The willow warbler is more easily satisfied with a few trees, especially birch, and a little overgrown vegetation for a nest-site. It will even breed in a narrow belt of trees beside a road or railway line.

In winter the job of identification is much easier because, while the willow warbler invariably winters in tropical Africa, the chiffchaff, like the blackcap, can survive a European winter. Many go no further south than Spain or Portugal while a few, probably birds from northern Europe, winter in the British Isles. A 'willow-chiff' in the garden between October and March just has to be a chiffchaff. It will probably be in the company of a feeding party of tits but it is unlikely to join them at the bird-table, choosing rather to forage for food in the garden shrubs.

BLACKCAP *Sylvia atricapilla*

SIZE 140 mm—the same size as a robin.

STATUS AND DISTRIBUTION In summer, common throughout Britain (except for parts of Ireland and the far north of Scotland). Small numbers are found in Britain during winter.

IN GARDENS A not infrequent garden visitor in winter, sightings becoming more common in recent years; occasionally seen at bird-tables. Sometimes in gardens in summer.

The females and juveniles of this species cannot be confused with any other British bird, being fairly uniform grey with a chestnut-brown cap.

The male is similar except that he sports the black cap which gives the species its name. Unlike the rounded black cap of the coal, marsh and willow tits, the blackcap's is quite small and higher on the head.

The blackcap is hardy enough to survive the winter in southern and western Europe, although many individuals head further south to North Africa and some appear to cross the Sahara and winter in West Africa. Although in summer mainly an insect-eater, the blackcap has a varied diet switching in autumn and winter to berries and fruit. However, it is possible that the increased frequency of winter sightings in British gardens is a result of the proliferation of bird-tables rather than an actual growth in the winter population of this species.

In summer, there are many more blackcaps in Britain, but it is not likely to be seen in the average garden then unless the garden and its surroundings approximate to the blackcap's natural woodland habitat and thus provide a breeding territory. It would need to be a fairly large, well-wooded garden with plenty of dense ground-cover such as brambles. But blackcaps may set up their territory in quite small copses, in overgrown corners of town parks and, in wooded suburbs, in the tangled vegetation of an empty building plot. It is one of the few birds to find conditions to its liking in the dark depths of rhododendron 'jungles'.

Because they remain well hidden in thick vegetation for much of the time, the best clue to their presence will be the male's splendid song: a rich, fluid performance, the notes tumbling over one another in a mellow stream. The song may lack the extraordinary variety of the nightingale but compares very favourably for richness and melody. The warning call, a sharp 'tack tack', is also very distinctive.

GARDEN WARBLER *Sylvia borin*

SIZE 140 mm—the same size as a robin.

STATUS AND DISTRIBUTION A summer visitor only. Fairly common throughout Britain except northern Scotland and Ireland.

IN GARDENS In spite of its name, very unlikely to appear in the vast majority of gardens.

This bird is mentioned primarily in an attempt to clear the confusion caused by its name. It is not really a garden bird at all: only in areas where it is very common does it breed in or near the occasional country garden. Like the blackcap, it is fundamentally a bird of thickly wooded areas with dense ground cover but unlike that close relative, it never over-winters in Britain, migrating much further south to tropical Africa.

In appearance it could be taken for a blackcap without a cap. It is uniform grey all over, though paler below than above, lacking any stripes, streaks or distinguishing features of any kind. What it lacks in colourful plumage, it makes up for many times over with its very fine song, an ebullient thrusting stream of mellow notes very similar to the blackcap's. Although ways of distinguishing the two songs are often described, even experts are frequently deceived and a definite identification without a sighting of the songster is difficult.

Beware of identifying a plain colourless bird in your garden as a garden warbler. It is much more likely to be a dull chiffchaff or willow warbler. Check the size carefully (the two birds just mentioned are smaller, about the size of a blue tit) and look for an eyestripe: the garden warbler has no visible markings whatsoever, not even the faintest eyestripe, whereas chiffchaffs and willow warblers show a pale eyestripe, even though this may be difficult to discern in some individuals. If still in doubt, it is necessary to remind oneself that a garden warbler is rarely seen in a garden.

WHITETHROAT *Sylvia communis*

SIZE   140 mm.

STATUS AND DISTRIBUTION   A summer visitor. Found throughout the British Isles.

IN GARDENS   Not likely in the majority of gardens but may breed in a few larger, thickly overgrown gardens. May occur briefly in gardens on migration, particularly in late summer and autumn.

This bird haunts overgrown tangles on rough ground, thorny thickets and hedgerows and woodland edges. The male whitethroat is extremely prominent in early summer as he often sings from a high perch—even a telegraph wire—and indulges in a spectacular, dancing song flight. In late summer soft fruit may attract a bird on passage into a garden.

The whitethroat (left) and the greyer-looking lesser whitethroat are occasional visitors to a few gardens, particularly in late summer.

The whitethroat has a warm brown back and wings; the male's head is pale grey; the female's brown or grey-brown. The lesser whitethroat, a closely related species, *Sylvia curruca*, has a grey back and wings and a dark grey or black patch near the eye on the side of the head which can make the bird appear to have a black cap.

Until its population crash in the late 60s and early 70s (a result of severe drought in the birds' winter quarters) the whitethroat was the most plentiful of all the warblers in Britain. The lesser whitethroat, which was not affected in this way, is more common in parts of south-east England but less numerous elsewhere in Britain and absent from Ireland and most of Scotland.

PIED FLYCATCHER *Ficedula hypoleuca*

SIZE 125 mm—slightly smaller than a robin.
STATUS AND DISTRIBUTION A summer visitor breeding almost exclusively in western and northern counties of England, southern and central Scotland—and Wales, which is its stronghold in Britain.
IN GARDENS Much less common in gardens than spotted flycatchers: breeds in a few large country gardens and orchards in the areas mentioned above. Elsewhere recorded in small numbers on migration, mainly in late April/early May, even in gardens and parks in large towns and cities. Uses nest-boxes.

No bird is more addicted to nest-boxes than the pied flycatcher. If given the choice of a natural hole in a tree or a hole-type nest box, it will almost invariably choose the artificial site. As a result, it has proved possible in some regions to boost the pied flycatcher's local population greatly and to bring about a spread in its distribution where new areas adjacent to its strongholds have been successfully colonised. Yet, for all this, as well as a considerable degree of tameness, the pied flycatcher is primarily a bird of woodland rather than gardens.

With his boldly contrasting plumage, the male pied flycatcher is one of the most attractive of summer visitors: the breast and underparts clean white, the back, tail and wings black except for white wing bars and a white spot on the forehead. The female is more creamy where the male is white and dull brown where he is black. However, in late summer and autumn the male's black is replaced by dark brown, making him look rather like the female.

The song of the pied flycatcher is cheerful but rather brief and abrupt, consisting only of about six notes: 'tree-tree-tree-tew-tew-tree', or variations about that theme. Its call, a sharp, piercing 'whit', is often heard when the bird is agitated.

The tail is repeatedly raised and lowered slowly and the wings dropped when the bird is perching, in particular just after it has alighted. This species has the typical pert bearing of a flycatcher but does not look nearly as upright as the spotted flycatcher, nor does it display the same darting flight in pursuit of flying insects. Although insects are caught in mid-air, it is with a rapid fluttering flight lacking the neat, graceful control of the spotted flycatcher's. For much of the time in its feeding habits, the pied flycatcher more closely resembles the robin or redstart, picking caterpillars off foliage or dropping down onto some insect on the ground from a convenient look-out perch.

SPOTTED FLYCATCHER *Muscicapa striata*

SIZE 140 mm—the same size as a robin.
STATUS AND DISTRIBUTION A common summer visitor throughout the British Isles. With the swift, it is the last of the migrants to arrive in early May.
IN GARDENS Often nests close to human habitation, even against the walls of houses; quite common in gardens in some areas. May pass through gardens on migration. Uses nest-boxes.

The spotted flycatcher is a delightful bird despite its modest colours. The head and upperparts are a dull grey-brown, the chest and underparts creamy with the few brown speckles just visible around the throat and on the forehead.

The appeal of this bird lies in its behaviour rather than appearance, although the pert upright stance and slim straight beak lend its general bearing a certain charm. Its dazzling quick flight is quite unlike that of any other British bird. It flits out time and time again from the same perch, dashing, twisting and turning this way and that before returning to the original perch or to one very close by. Sometimes one can hear the 'click' as the beak snaps shut on the victim.

Primarily a bird of woodland edges, small copses or country gardens, it breeds in some town parks and suburban gardens where there are a few mature trees. The song is an odd little chatter, rather squeaky and scratchy and lacking in strength.

The spotted flycatcher frequents gardens in summer. This nest in ivy is fairly typical.

MEADOW PIPIT *Anthus pratensis*

SIZE   145 mm.

STATUS AND DISTRIBUTION   A partial migrant, found throughout most of the British Isles, at all times of the year.

IN GARDENS   Rare in summer; occasionally in winter.

The meadow pipit is normally a bird of open country, moors, heaths, rough pastures, hills and even mountains. However, meadow pipits may desert their traditional habitat in winter and resort to various kinds of grassed areas, including such places as playing fields, golf courses, large lawns around sewage works, factories and industrial estates, as well as open-plan housing estates.

When visiting a garden, the meadow pipit hops around the lawn and forages for small food items underneath the bird-table. It is a similar size to a dunnock and may at a casual glance be taken for a very pale version of that species or a small, delicate song thrush. An inexperienced observer may dismiss it as a sparrow but the streaked buff-brown upper parts, cream breast flecked with black and, more especially, the slim beak should prevent confusion.

REED BUNTING *Emberiza schoeniclus*

SIZE   150 mm—marginally larger than a house sparrow.

STATUS AND DISTRIBUTION   A partial migrant which can be found throughout Britain at all times of year.

IN GARDENS   Only outside the breeding season, and then infrequent.

The reed bunting is a waterside bird, but outside the breeding season this species is commonly seen on farmland and other stretches of dry, cultivated land. It is not likely to visit gardens in built-up parts but it is being recorded more often at bird-tables where it may feed on the ground or some-times on top of the bird-table itself. Vegetation around the garden pond is also an attraction.

In the breeding season, the male is almost un-mistakable with his jet black head and bib divided by a bold white moustachial stripe and nape. Out-side the breeding season, which is the only time this species is likely to be encountered in a garden, the male is much less striking and more closely resembles the hen, although it is usually possible to see the black head and throat mark-ings showing faintly through the dull feather tips. In winter a reed bunting might be confused at first glance with a sparrow, except for the dark moustachial stripe. The tail is longer than a sparrow's, however, and is simultaneously flicked and fanned out so that the white outer tail feathers are then extremely prominent.

TREE SPARROW *Passer montanus*

SIZE   140 mm—fractionally smaller and slimmer than the house sparrow.

STATUS AND DISTRIBUTION   A year-round resident throughout much of Britain but unevenly distri-buted. Most abundant in central and eastern parts of Britain. Much less common than the house sparrow. Absent from or uncommon in northern Scotland, most inland areas of Ireland and parts of Wales and south-west England.

IN GARDENS   Uncommon in most gardens. May visit gardens on the edges of towns or in farming areas. Uses nest-boxes.

The tree sparrow merits only a brief description here, by way of distinguishing it from the house sparrow, for in many respects it is not a garden bird. One is more likely to encounter it in copses, hedgerows and orchards in agricultural areas or feeding on the ground in open fields.

In appearance, the cock and hen tree sparrow are alike and can be told from the house sparrow by their chestnut crown, which extends down the back of the head, and black crescent behind the white cheek. Both male and female house sparrow lack these characteristics.

The favourite nest-site of this species is a hole in a tree, but holes of all kinds are used in old ruins, cliffs, quarries and occasionally in build-ings. Like the house sparrow, it sometimes makes a nest among the branches of a tree or bush, usually if a suitable hole is not available.

Tree sparrow (top left); cock house sparrow (top right); hen house sparrow (centre right); dunnock (bottom).

HOUSE SPARROW *Passer domesticus*

SIZE   145 mm.
STATUS AND DISTRIBUTION   A very common year-round resident throughout Britain, anywhere near human habitation.
IN GARDENS   Very common. Visits bird-tables. Uses nest-boxes.

With the exception of the feral pigeon, no bird has more fully adapted to city life than the house sparrow, so much so that it is rarely encountered anywhere away from human activity. Because it is so prominent in such places, many erroneously consider the house sparrow the most common British bird. But there are vast areas of woodland and open country where it is rarely seen and where wrens, chaffinches, robins, blackbirds and other birds are much more numerous all the year round.

The appearance of this bird is familiar to all, but it is worth noting the male's markings: a large black bib below the beak and a rather grubby-looking grey crown and rump. The females and juveniles lack any such distinguishing marks, although there is an indistinct pale stripe through the eye.

The sparrow has the heavy bill of a seed-eater but it has acquired a taste for anything edible which man discards or places on bird-tables. In some gardens, house sparrows are so common that other birds are shouldered out, and the species shows its versatility by feeding at peanut holders. It has no song as such, except for a repetition of its familiar unmusical chirruping.

In spite of its almost continuous proximity to man and the habits of a few individuals in town parks who have learned that people eating sandwiches are a ready source of food, the house sparrow is a wary bird. This may have something to do with man's long-standing hostility towards the species because of its frequent raids on summer grain in country districts. Elsewhere, it regularly attacks peas, and seedlings on the suburban vegetable patch, while in the flower borders crocuses, especially yellow ones, and other flowers such as primroses are often destroyed.

DUNNOCK *Prunella modularis*

SIZE   145 mm—a fraction larger than a robin.
STATUS AND DISTRIBUTION   A year-round resident throughout Britain, especially in woodland, but wherever there are trees, bushes and hedges.
IN GARDENS   Very common in most types of garden. Visits bird-tables.

No garden bird is more often wrongly identified than the dunnock. It is frequently dismissed by the average person as 'just another sparrow', even though it is not related to the sparrows in any way. Its second name, hedge-sparrow, only adds to the confusion, as does its habit of feeding amongst sparrows on the garden lawn. Yet in the food it eats, the nest it builds, the sounds it makes and even its appearance it is quite different from a sparrow in a number of ways. The dunnock does not flock, as the sparrow does, and, when the sparrows fly off, the dunnock will probably stay.

The beak is delicate, like a robin's, compared to the thick, rather heavy bill of the sparrow, and the head and throat are a not unattractive slate-grey, whereas the only grey on a house sparrow is the small dirty-grey crown on the cock. The dunnock's flanks are flecked whereas a sparrow's are not and its iris is orange or red-brown. The dunnock is mainly an insect-eating bird in summer, turning to small seeds in winter, so it is more choosy than the sparrows about what it eats at the bird-table, preferring softer, smaller items.

The dunnock's light, slightly metallic song is delicate and musical, one of the most attractive songs among garden birds. Although rather short and lacking in volume, it puts to shame the monotonous twitters of the sparrows. And few sights are more lovely than a dunnock's nest with a full clutch of sky-blue eggs.

SISKIN *Carduelis spinus*

SIZE   115 mm—considerably smaller than both chaffinch and greenfinch.
STATUS AND DISTRIBUTION   In summer breeds in Scotland and Ireland and, less commonly, in scattered parts of England and Wales. Occurs anywhere in Britain in winter.

This juvenile goldfinch has not yet acquired the red, black and white face markings of its elders.

IN GARDENS   In some winters, rarely seen, in others very common. Visits bird-tables.

The siskin is very much a woodland bird, especially dependent on spruce, pine, birch and alder. The British summer population is augmented in winter by large numbers of siskins from northern Europe, especially Scandinavia, but these numbers vary from year to year. Often they will be seen acrobatically suspending themselves like tits from branches in birches and alders. When the natural food supply is short, siskins become much more common at bird-tables, hanging from peanuts with the tits and greenfinches. At such times, they prove extremely tame, apparently very reluctant to forsake their new-found food-source: some will continue feeding as humans walk past the bird-table only a pace or two away.

The male siskin is fairly easy to identify with his yellow and black markings and a distinctive black cap. The female is sometimes confused with female chaffinches (which are larger and do not usually feed on peanut holders) and greenfinches (which are larger and unstreaked). She has an over-all streaked, yellowy look but is less colourful

than the cock bird and lacks his black cap. Nevertheless, she is strongly flecked with black on her pale flanks and her wing bars are lemon yellow.

The pleasant twittering song is not very likely to be heard in the average garden but in March or April the birds may be seen gathering together in chattering groups making a communal sound not unlike an aviary of budgerigars.

GOLDFINCH *Carduelis carduelis*

SIZE   120 mm—a fairly small finch, smaller than a robin.

STATUS AND DISTRIBUTION   Found throughout Britain, except northern Scotland, at all times of the year. Quite common.

IN GARDENS   Quite common but visits are irregular. Often nests in gardens in country districts. More likely to visit in winter when flocks roam in search of food.

When the goldfinch is perching, the red, white and black face is especially striking and the black wing and tail feathers, pale underparts and warm light tan back all catch the eye more than the relatively small area of gold on the wing. When the bird is seen flying, though, the golden wing bars show to good advantage and even at a distance are the most dazzling feature, explaining why its name gives emphasis to the gold. The sexes are alike but young birds are easy to identify as they have the yellow wing bars but lack the striped red, white and black head.

In summer the goldfinch is primarily a bird of open country, farmland and fields dotted with bushes and copses, being most frequently seen feeding on the seed heads of dandelion and thistles. However, this species frequently enters towns in autumn and winter and flocks may be encountered in heavily built-up areas if there are plenty of weeds to plunder. A group of goldfinches frequently draws attention to itself, as do many of the finches, when they fly past or alight on a nearby bush, all giving the call note, in this case a soft 'wit-wit-wit'. The male's song is an attractive assemblage of call notes musically strung together.

When feeding, the goldfinch's behaviour is

similar to that of the tit family, restlessly flitting from plant to plant, now hanging head down, now perched on top of a thistle or flower.

LESSER REDPOLL *Acanthis flammea cabaret*

SIZE   130 mm.

STATUS AND DISTRIBUTION   Found throughout the British Isles at all times of the year. More abundant as a breeding bird in the north.

IN GARDENS   Irregular but not infrequent. More likely to be seen in winter.

The lesser redpoll is commonly seen in a mixed feeding flock consisting of its own kind, siskins and perhaps a few tits. Hanging upside down, like a trapeze-artist, from the slenderest of twigs in a birch or alder, it may at first be mistaken for a tit, for it shares their lightness and agility though not their bright colours. In fact, closer scrutiny will reveal a bird which looks more like a lightweight, delicate sparrow except for the red forehead sported by the adults. The male also has a pink flush on his light, speckled breast.

In the autumn and winter, redpolls move over large areas in search of food and indeed, like other tree-feeding finches, it is one of the species given to irruptions, when thousands of birds spread far and wide. Many of the British redpolls move south and east and may leave the country to spend the winter in Holland, France and Spain, while, at the same time, being replaced by large numbers arriving from Scandinavia and other regions of northern Europe. The movements and irruptions are regulated largely by the tree crops, particularly of birch and alder. If there are ample supplies of birch seeds, redpolls will not move far but, in other winters, they may travel great distances and the population in an area offering an abundance of food may multiply many times over from one year to the next. Like other irruptive species, redpolls, adapted as they are to a nomadic existence, settling in any area which provides for their needs, have virtually no 'homing' instincts. Whereas most of the garden birds return to breed in the area where they were born, redpolls may raise their young hundreds of miles from their place of birth.

They will feed anywhere where their favourite trees are found and this often includes suburban parks, roadside hedges, waste-ground, waterside trees and gardens. They are usually seen feeding above the ground in trees in willows, sallows and conifers as well as their favoured birch and alder but they sometimes drop down to pick seeds off the ground on lawns, flower beds and vegetable patches, where their brown streaked upper parts make them extremely difficult to pick out against the soil. On these occasions, their pale buff-coloured wing-bars may be the most prominent feature and an aid to identification.

BRAMBLING *Fringilla montifringilla*

SIZE   145 mm.

STATUS AND DISTRIBUTION   A winter visitor, except for a handful of breeding attempts in Scotland.

IN GARDENS   Rare.

The brambling is usually encountered in flocks, often in the company of its close relative the chaffinch. In size it is only a fraction shorter than the chaffinch with which it has other similarities, particularly in its breeding behaviour. Unfortunately few British bird-watchers are able to enjoy fully the male's splendid summer plumage for, by April, most bramblings have left Britain and returned to their breeding territories in Scandinavia and Finland. In winter the two sexes look rather similar and could be mistaken for immature cock chaffinches though the colouring around the throat and chest is more orange than the pinky-red of the chaffinch. The best method of identifying bramblings is to wait until they fly up from the ground. Then it is possible to see that they lack the chaffinch's bright white outer tail feathers but have instead a very striking white patch on the rump. From late January onwards, however, some of the cocks begin to look rather different as the dull grey-brown feathers on their heads and backs begin to wear away at the tips to reveal the black beneath. This can make them look rather untidy at first but, as the breeding season approaches, many of them begin to assume their fine summer plumage.

It is usually at this time, in late winter, that bramblings may venture into gardens if their beloved beech mast supplies are becoming depleted. They will eat a variety of seeds at bird-tables and have, on a number of occasions, been recorded taking peanuts from hanging nut-baskets.

CHAFFINCH *Fringilla coelebs*

SIZE 150 mm—a little larger than a house sparrow.
STATUS AND DISTRIBUTION Common throughout Britain at all times of the year.
IN GARDENS Very common. A regular at bird-tables. Sometimes nests in gardens.

Because the chaffinch is not so common in large towns as the house sparrow, many are surprised to learn that it is much more widespread throughout the country. Unlike the sparrow, it is just as, or even more, abundant away from human settlement and one of the most common birds in Britain. In car parks in country districts it replaces the city sparrow soliciting for food from picnickers, even taking food from the hand. In woodland everywhere its song is ever-present in spring and on most farmland only the blackbird is more common.

The chaffinch is fairly easy to identify, though often confused with the bullfinch by the inexperienced birdwatcher. The male has a blue-grey head and nape (not a black crown), pink cheeks and chest and a green rump (unlike the bullfinch's white rump). The back is browner, the outer tail feathers are white, as are the two wing bars, which show as white shoulder patches when the wings are flat to the body. The female has the same bold, black and white markings on wing and tail but is mainly buff, brown and grey on her body. The white flashes on wings and tail are easily discerned and often the most noticeable feature as a group of chaffinches fly up from the ground and disappear into a tree.

Chaffinches are common at bird-tables, usually feeding in small groups on the ground, though very occasionally a few individuals manage, not without some difficulty, to cling on to peanut

holders. The bullfinch, by contrast, rarely visits bird-tables, is hardly ever seen in the company of more than one other bullfinch, normally its mate, and does not usually feed on the ground. The chaffinch's most familiar sound is its call, 'pink, pink', the single note being deliberately uttered. The song is slightly rattly but strong and hearty and not unmusical.

BULLFINCH *Pyrrhula pyrrhula*

SIZE 150 mm—fractionally larger than a house sparrow.
STATUS AND DISTRIBUTION Found throughout Britain, except the far north, at all times of the year in woods, copses, hedgerows, orchards. Nowhere uncommon but unevenly distributed.
IN GARDENS Variable but quite common in some gardens, especially country gardens and gardens with fruit trees.

Although one of the most colourful of British birds, the bullfinch is not popular. It has a reputation, not without justification, for causing considerable damage to fruit crops in some areas where it feeds on the buds of plum, apple and pear trees in late winter and spring. A garden forsythia, too, bare of blossom is a legacy of a brief earlier visit by a pair of bullfinches, for this bird, although sometimes seen in small flocks especially in large orchards, is almost invariably encountered in gardens in twos, and pairs appear to remain together for much of the year. Its squat, rounded build does not give it charm; it is not a graceful bird and its movements when feeding are ponderous compared to the tit-like agility of some other finches such as goldfinch and siskin.

Yet it is impossible not to admire the marvellous livery of the bullfinch. The male has a brilliant cherry-red front, alongside which the chaffinch's breast looks positively drab; the cap, tail and wings are jet black (although there is a clear white wing bar) and the back is an attractive pale blue-grey. The female is similarly marked but her front is a pleasing mauve-brown and her back grey-brown. She shares with the cock bird the startlingly white rump, which is such a feature of the bullfinch when viewed from behind

The male bullfinch is splendidly marked, the female rather less colourful. The cock chaffinch (top right) is less striking than the male bullfinch and lacks the bold black cap—but is much brighter than his dull, grey and buff female (bottom).

as it flies off—as useful an identification as the white rump of the much larger jay, for, like that bird, the bullfinch is rather shy and often just glimpsed as it dives for cover. When out of sight the bullfinch will usually betray its presence only by its melancholy call 'pew-pew'.

GREENFINCH *Carduelis chloris*

SIZE   150 mm—fractionally larger than a sparrow.

STATUS AND DISTRIBUTION   Common throughout Britain at all times of the year.

IN GARDENS   Very common. A regular at birdtables. Sometimes nests in gardens.

Found almost anywhere where there are trees and bushes, the greenfinch is an adaptable bird; apart from the siskin, it is the only finch to have really mastered the technique of hanging onto peanut holders at bird-tables.

The cock bird is an unstreaked yellowy green all over, with black on the wings and tail feathers; some of the flight feathers are lemon-yellow as are some feathers at each side of the tail. As a greenfinch flies off, the tail is fanned out, giving one the impression that there is much more yellow on the bird than there really is. The females and young birds are similarly marked but a dull brown-green rather than green, though the female's colour varies in brightness with maturity. The heavy bill, which is large even by finch standards, deals easily with seeds which comprise the main part of its diet. Other food items, including insects in summer, are eaten.

The song is a combination of a twitter and an

odd drawn-out wheeze, as if the bird has some chest congestion. The call, a pleasant, light twittering, is often heard, especially as the birds fly away from a garden, as if pulling the flock together.

HAWFINCH *Coccothraustes coccothraustes*

SIZE   180 mm—the largest British finch.

STATUS AND DISTRIBUTION   Largely confined to England, a few parts of Wales and isolated locations in Scotland. It is most abundant in the south-east corner of England.

IN GARDENS   Has been recorded nesting in large gardens, though this is rare; too nervous to visit bird-tables regularly.

With its huge bill, which can crunch a plum or cherry-stone to reach the kernel, the hawfinch is unlikely to be confused with any other bird—that is if the observer has a good view. For the hawfinch is an extremely retiring and secretive bird in Britain. In its favourite haunts (deciduous woods and large orchards, especially cherry) it is so quiet and unobtrusive that often one only sees it as it flies away when surprised. Then, its very bold white wing bars and chunky build are the most noticeable features. Occasionally it may be seen flying overhead and then its wide-bodied fuselage is even more apparent. It is a shame that more people do not enjoy a better look at what is, in spite of its heavy-headed look, a most attractive bird: chestnut head and rump, dark tan back, black and white wings and pale grey nape.

The hawfinch usually seeks more private sites than gardens for its nest, high up in deciduous trees in woodland or old fruit trees in large orchards. In those parts of the country where it is more common, the hawfinch occasionally takes nuts and seeds from bird-tables.

HOUSE MARTIN *Delichon urbica*

SIZE   125 mm.

STATUS AND DISTRIBUTION   A common summer visitor to all parts of Britain except the far north of Scotland.

IN GARDENS   Frequently seen around houses, even in towns. Nests under the eaves of houses (as well as a few 'natural' sites such as cliffs).

The house martin should not be confused with any other bird with its dazzling white belly and very distinctive white rump. It is rather chunky compared to the slim and graceful swallow, lacking the long, forked tail and the very long wings. (A young swallow with its short tail has a similar shape but lacks the white rump.) The upperparts look jet black but are, in fact, blue-black. The legs and feet are covered with white, down-like feathering.

The nest, invariably placed on the outside of a building, is a mud cup, but unlike the swallow's open bowl it is almost completely enclosed, except for the small entrance-hole. Nests are often close together in colonies, sometimes several side by side actually touching each other.

As the birds fly overhead feeding, the two-note call, 'chirrip', is often heard, not unlike the pied wagtail's 'chizz-it'. There is also a short, twittering song, less exuberant than the swallow's.

When hunting for insects, the house martin often joins swallows and swifts over water but, unlike those birds, it can also be seen darting around just above a clump of trees catching insects very close to the foliage.

SWALLOW *Hirundo rustica*

SIZE   190 mm—including long tail.

STATUS AND DISTRIBUTION   A common summer visitor to all parts of Britain.

IN GARDENS   May be seen overhead from any garden but much less common in built-up areas than swift or house martin. Nests in country gardens are very common; occasionally nests in suburban gardens.

Few sights epitomise summer more than swallows skimming low across a river or lake, or flicking past grazing cows while hawking for insects just above the ground.

The swallow is told from the swift and the house martin by its very long tail streamers, its deep gun-metal blue back and wings and the

The comical and charming pied wagtail is a common bird around buildings everywhere.

rusty red throat and forehead. The belly and some of the underwing feathers are creamy. When the tail is spread, a row of white dots at the tip of each tail feather stands out brightly. From July onwards, young swallows can be seen flying with very short tails, otherwise looking like pale versions of the adults.

Whereas the house martin nests outside, the swallow usually nests inside buildings, although 'outdoor' nests may be found, for instance, underneath bridges. The nest is a cup of mud and straw, usually high up in a shed, barn, garage, or any kind of outbuilding but, in a low-roofed building, the nest may be only a metre or so above the ground. The nest may be placed on a beam or shelf but if that is not possible it will be stuck to the side of a beam without any support underneath. Several nests may be close together in the same building.

Around a nest the 'sip, sip' calls are given repeatedly but can be heard anywhere as the birds fly past. The song, a pleasant cheerful stream of twitters, interspersed with a few squeaks, scratches and little rattles, may be delivered from a wire or in flight.

SWIFT *Apus apus*

SIZE   165 mm—larger than house martin; body length similar to swallow's but the tail of the swallow is much longer.
STATUS AND DISTRIBUTION   A common summer visitor to all parts of Britain except in the far north where it is less common.
IN GARDENS   Frequently seen around houses; many nests are in roofs and crevices in older houses or other old buildings such as churches and castles, frequently in the centre of towns and cities. Usually the same sites are used year after year.

Both the house martin's English name and its scientific title Delichon urbica *indicate how closely this species is associated with urban man. Here a house martin has just commenced nest-building.*

Swifts are easily told from swallows and house martins in flight, being very dark brown, almost black, all over, except for a pale throat. The other two have white undersides. With their extremely long, curved wings and short tails they look like dashing black bows. Often, especially in late summer, parties of swifts join together to dive and swoop around the buildings of a town, screaming and squealing their unmistakable unnerving calls.

The life cycle of this bird is extraordinary: it never voluntarily alights on the ground, not even to gather nest-material. Instead, air-borne particles of grass and other vegetation, as well as feathers, are caught in flight. The swift is hardly able to support itself on its feeble legs, let alone walk, so it alights only at the nest.

The feet are unique, with all four toes hooked and pointing forwards, so the bird can in fact hook itself onto the side of a building while, for example, working its way under the eaves of a house to its nest. The swift's life, apart from time spent incubating eggs or feeding young in the nest, is spent totally in flight. Feeding, sleeping and mating all take place on the wing (although mating also takes place at the nest).

PIED WAGTAIL *Motacilla alba yarrellii*

SIZE   180 mm—roughly the size of a robin, except for the long tail.
STATUS AND DISTRIBUTION   Found throughout Britain the year round.
IN GARDENS   Regularly found around housing, summer and winter, but visits bird-tables only sporadically. Prefers tarmac-covered or paved areas to lawns, open spaces to enclosed gardens. Uses nest-boxes.

Few birds are more closely associated with human activity than the pied wagtail. Its favoured haunts are farmyards, freight depots, railway stations, car parks, school playgrounds, shopping centres, factories, in fact anywhere where there are buildings and open spaces, preferably with a tarmac surface. On roads it is sometimes almost suicidal in its behaviour, flitting just ahead of an approaching car. Yet it is far less frequently a victim of a car strike than the blackbird, for example. In winter, pied wagtails gather around areas of water such as rivers, reservoirs, ponds and sewage-works.

Few birds spend more time in the open than this bird and possibly no garden bird is seen more often on the ground. It never hops but often accelerates into a short sprint in pursuit of an insect. The head is forever tapping, the tail continually bouncing (rather than wagging like a dog's). It is rarely still, fussy and capricious in movement, its route random and unpredictable. Even when approaching its nest with food for the nestlings, it will frequently walk or trot the last few metres, often taking an unnecessary detour and usually using a different route each time.

In its smart black and white uniform, the pied wagtail's haphazard meanderings and sudden spurts remind one of an over-attentive waiter. In winter the bold black and white patterning is not so clearly marked, with less distinct black around the breast. The sexes are similar but the female's patterning looks more blotchy and her back is grey- rather than jet-black.

This species seems incapable of flying in silence. Its undulating flight is always accompanied by regular 'chizz-it' calls, coinciding, as a rule, with a few wing-beats.

The bouncing of the tail appears to serve no purpose neither being used as part of any mating display nor assisting the bird's balance. Yet it is such a deeply-rooted instinct that even quite small nestlings will bob their little stubs before their tail feathers have developed.

GREY WAGTAIL *Motacilla cinerea*

SIZE   180 mm.

STATUS AND DISTRIBUTION   It may be found in any area of the British Isles at all times of the year but is less common in regions, such as eastern England, which lack fast-flowing streams.

IN GARDENS   Sporadic visits, normally in cold weather.

In summer the grey wagtail is almost always found near swiftly-flowing streams where it nests in cavities of various kinds, on concealed ledges, among tree roots, under bridges and in similar situations.

In autumn a proportion of the British population leaves for France, Spain and Portugal, returning in early spring while others move, usually in a southerly direction, within the British Isles. Some of these spend the winter period near the coast while a few are found near ponds, lakes, reservoirs, on swampy terrains and around sewage works. Almost as unafraid of man as the pied wagtail, the grey wagtail is not infrequently seen in towns, around human dwellings and areas of work. It shares other features with its more familiar relative: the bobbing tail and head, deeply undulating flight and a 'chizz-it' call. The size is the same but the tail of this bird is slightly longer and it is rather more graceful.

Of course the main difference is in the colour. The grey wagtail acquires its name from its smart light-grey back and wings but the most striking feature is the lemon yellow of the underparts, which sometimes leads to its being confused with the summer visitor, the yellow wagtail. Both sexes have a faint white stripe through the eye: the cock has a striking black throat and bib.

Gardens which receive a visit from this bird are probably fairly close to a river or lake but this does not have to be the case. One garden which was visited by a grey wagtail on several days for three successive winters is at least 2·5 km from the nearest water, and to reach it the bird would have had to cross several fields, a road, some houses and a wood. The bird in question (although, naturally, it could have been different birds on each occasion) pottered around on the lawn in search of small seeds and insects and spent some of the time picking up small items of food from the ground beneath the bird-table.

STARLING *Sturnus vulgaris*

SIZE   215 mm—rather smaller than a blackbird.

STATUS AND DISTRIBUTION   Found throughout the year in all parts of Britain, being common anywhere, even in city centres.

IN GARDENS   Very common. Often nests in houses. A regular at bird-tables. May use a larger nest-box with a suitable-sized hole.

It is hard to imagine a more boisterous and belligerent bird than the starling. Rarely quiet, even when nesting, often in large restless flocks in winter, messy and raucous when eating, starlings make their presence felt wherever they go. This presence is not always welcomed: well-stocked bird-tables with sufficient food to last a large number of small birds an entire day can be cleared in minutes; nests under eaves, in lofts and chimneys are invariably noisy and insanitary places.

Yet, in spite of all this, the starling has a certain appeal: the summer coat has a splendid metallic sheen turning from green, to black, to mauve as the light catches it. In winter, it is boldly speckled with white but retains some of the iridescence. The yellow bill of summer turns dark in winter; the tail is short compared to a blackbird's. And the starling's waddling, high-stepping walk is comical, as is its clumsy and ungainly behaviour at a bird-table. No other bird could accidentally fall backwards over the edge of a bird-table!

The shapeless, somewhat asthmatic song is a mixture of many rattling and chuckling notes with some whistles thrown in, usually delivered from a high perch, a tree, building or telephone wire. The most commonly heard call is a rather raucous squawk.

The starling usually feeds on the ground in fields and on lawns, repeatedly driving its long bill into the ground with its mandibles apart to probe for insect larvae, especially leatherjackets. Elsewhere it will take caterpillars from trees to feed nestlings, take fruit and berries while still on the tree, and will scavenge almost anywhere for almost anything, even on rubbish tips.

ROBIN *Erithacus rubecula*

SIZE   140 mm—with the redstarts, one of the smallest of the thrush family.
STATUS AND DISTRIBUTION Very common throughout Britain except for the most remote and barren parts, at all times of the year.
IN GARDENS   A 'regular'—summer and winter. Visits bird-tables readily. Uses nest-boxes.

The robin, so familiar to all that detailed description is superfluous, is possibly the best-loved of all garden birds. Its sweet, liquid song, along with the blackbird's, is probably the most familiar to the average person. While the main features are well-known and need not be rehearsed here, the less prominent details are worth noticing, such as the delicate silvery-grey border around the famous red breast and the fact that the red extends upwards so that the throat and face are also red.

The two sexes are identical in appearance though recently-fledged birds seen in gardens between May and July lack the red breast, having instead a speckled front hinting at their relationship to the thrush family. One pair of adults can go on after their first brood are fledged, to rear a second and even a third brood in the same summer.

The general posture is alert and upright, and no bird eyes the ground for a prospective meal with more sharp-eyed intentness, head cocked, tail bobbing and wings flicking in anticipation. It is this perkiness combined with an extremely trusting nature which gives this bird much of its appeal. Yet in its natural haunts in woodland it is far more retiring, and in other parts of Europe it is only known as a shy woodland bird.

It is basically an insect-eater, catching much of its food by dropping down from a perch a little above the ground, although it will also look for food by hopping about on the ground; in winter it will take almost anything from the bird-table.

REDSTART *Phoenicurus phoenicurus*

SIZE   140 mm—the size of a robin.
STATUS AND DISTRIBUTION   A summer visitor to most parts of Britain except Ireland. Very local: in some areas very common indeed, in others rarely seen.
IN GARDENS   In certain redstart areas, will breed in or near wooded gardens. Elsewhere, may pay a fleeting visit on migration. Uses nest-boxes.

No bird can light up a woodland glade or garden quite like the redstart with its quivering fiery-red tail seeming to reflect the sunlight. In behaviour

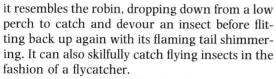

In Britain, the redstart favours woodland edges and wooded, hilly districts and only occasionally appears in gardens. The male (left) is extremely colourful but the warm browns of the female (right) lend her considerable charm.

it resembles the robin, dropping down from a low perch to catch and devour an insect before flitting back up again with its flaming tail shimmering. It can also skilfully catch flying insects in the fashion of a flycatcher.

The brilliantly marked cock redstart is unmistakable. The bright orange-red of the chest and underparts extends to the rump and the tail, contrasting strongly with the slate-blue back and jet-black face and throat. The white forehead is a final distinguishing feature. The female suffers by comparison but is nevertheless attractive with a light brown body and warm orange rump and tail.

The male has a rather short, weak song with a few scratchy notes which seem to die suddenly. The call is a louder and much more distinctive sound, a plaintive 'wheet', often followed by 'tuck' or 'tuck, tuck' if the bird is alarmed. Sometimes, in an area where several pairs are nesting close together, it seems that at least one pair is constantly agitated about something. Because neighbouring pairs then pick up and continue the alarm call, there are times when one is never out of hearing of the sound.

Though generally labelled a woodland bird, the redstart does not favour thick woodland, rather the margins of woods or large clearings and glades between scattered trees. Numbers have declined in some areas but there are 'boom'

summers for this species when they occupy territories not used for many years.

BLACK REDSTART *Phoenicurus ochruros*

SIZE   140 mm—same size as robin.
STATUS AND DISTRIBUTION   Rare, breeding mainly in the south-east, and also present in tiny numbers in winter in the south and south-west.
IN GARDENS   Very rare, despite its being extremely common in towns in many parts of Europe.

This bird has many similarities with the common redstart: it has the typical orange-red rump and tail of its kind with the central tail feathers duller, almost brown, so that when the tail is at rest and the feathers folded together, the red does not show very well. There is also the distinctive redstart 'shiver' of the tail and the conspicuous spreading and fanning of it in flight as the bird twists and brakes. The call note 'wit', sometimes attached to a harsh 'tack', is reminiscent of the redstart's insistent 'wheet-tuck', though the present species sounds sharper and less mournful. The song, however, is quite different: it begins with five high-pitched, whistling, rippling notes which are followed by what has been described as a sound like ball-bearings being shaken in a bag. The comparison with ball-bearings could not be more apt but the cascading rattle of notes in quick succession suggests that the ball-bearings are being tipped rapidly, one after another, into the bag rather than being shaken. In its feeding

The black redstart is very much a town bird. It is extremely rare in Britain but very common around man's buildings in several European countries. The male (right) is blacker than the female (left).

habits, the black redstart resembles the cock redstart in its fly-catching sallies but is even more swift and acrobatic, and the perch from which it launches itself is a chimney pot, roof top, telephone wire or television aerial rather than the branch of a tree. This species can hover very well and frequently chooses to do so, in the manner of a goldcrest, to pick insects from beneath eaves, guttering, ledges and balconies. Like the thrushes, robin and redstart, the black redstart is often active in twilight when it may hunt for insects attracted to street lights.

A comparison can also be drawn with the robin, based not just on the pert, upright, nervous-bobbing posture but also on its approachability and trusting nature. One wintering black redstart which came freely for biscuit crumbs and mealworms and became virtually hand-tame in a matter of a few days was as confiding as any robin in any British garden.

Like the robin, too, it is extremely territorial in winter as well as in summer. In southern Europe wintering black redstarts and robins are very common indeed: territorial disputes including fighting and singing may be regularly witnessed among both species.

In recent years, there have been signs of a gradual spread northwards and westwards across Britain and the bird has now colonised a few sites in northern England and Scotland. In Britain today, now that its favoured bombsites have disappeared, the black redstart breeds around factories, gas-works, power stations, docks, railway goods yards and haulage depots. It has been discussed here in some detail in the anticipation that one day this delightful bird may become as familiar to townsfolk in Britain as it is in some parts of Europe.

NIGHTINGALE *Luscinia megarhynchos*

SIZE   165 mm.

STATUS AND DISTRIBUTION   Summer visitor from April to August or September. Found almost exclusively south and east of a line drawn from the Humber through South Wales to the Devon/Cornwall border.

IN GARDENS   Rare.

The nightingale is rivalled perhaps only by the cuckoo as a bird of myth and legend, yet it is not a common bird, nowadays in Britain at least, and few people have heard its song; because of its habit of skulking deep in thick vegetation, only a tiny proportion of the population will have seen one, either. If they did see one, they would probably express disappointment, for it is an undistinguished bird in appearance: slightly larger than a sparrow, light creamy-buff below, plain reddish-brown above.

Large, rambling wooded gardens with a tangle of dense vegetation are the only ones a nightingale is likely to use so it only barely qualifies as a garden bird, though in France, Spain and in

The nightingale sometimes occurs in a few large country gardens in southern Britain. It is more common in some countries in Europe.

other countries in central and southern Europe it may be heard singing, in May and early June, from thickets around many houses and gardens.

Although the nightingale sings during the day, it is on a still night that it creates its most startling effect: the song is incredibly powerful and far-carrying and includes an extraordinary variety of notes. Even so, it lacks the mellow richness and rippling fluency of other songsters such as blackbird, blackcap and willow warbler—it is exciting and dramatic rather than beautiful. There are many people in Britain who are convinced that they have a nightingale singing near their homes, even in winter when all nightingales are south of the Sahara Desert. This confusion is caused by the habit among several garden birds, especially the robin, of singing when it is dark.

BLACKBIRD *Turdus merula*

SIZE   250 mm.
STATUS AND DISTRIBUTION   Very common throughout Britain at all times of the year.
IN GARDENS   A garden 'regular' both summer and winter. Uses bird-tables. Often nests close to a house.

With the exception of the robin, the blackbird is probably the most familiar of all garden birds and, like the robin, it is really a woodland bird which has found the suburban habitat created by

man as much to its liking as its natural one.

The appearance of the glossy cock blackbird with his bright yellow beak is well-known. But notice the splendid bright gold eye-ring which, like the beak, becomes brighter as the bird matures after its first year. The female of the species is less striking. It is not generally known that blackbirds are members of the thrush family but the hen blackbird gives evidence of this by her brown and cream speckled throat which causes her to be regularly identified as a dark brown song thrush.

A loud clucking, accompanied by a flicking of the wings and tail, is characteristic of the blackbird, as is its manner of alighting on a branch or garden fence, always raising and fanning its tail a moment after landing as if this aids braking.

When searching for food among dead leaves it makes a great deal of noise as leaves are tossed to left and right, so much so that one is often misled into thinking that a large mammal, a rabbit or even a fox, is moving around and rustling the vegetation. This ability to find food underneath the surface leaf-layer is especially useful to the bird when snow covers the ground or when the earth is frozen hard.

SONG THRUSH *Turdus philomelos*

SIZE   230 mm—slightly smaller than a blackbird.
STATUS AND DISTRIBUTION   Found in all parts of Britain throughout the year. Common in most areas.
IN GARDENS   Common at all times but variable according to area. Visits bird-tables.

In both woodland and farmland, the song thrush is one of the ten most common birds but it is thought of by many as primarily a garden bird. Rarely as tame as some blackbirds it nevertheless visits bird-tables freely and often nests very close to human activity.

Although it lacks bright colours, the song thrush is one of the most attractive garden birds, the subtle coffee and cream colouring making a pleasing combination. Compared to the larger mistle thrush, it is a darker bird with richer brown

Three members of the thrush family display the speckled breasts so typical of their kind. A female blackbird (top) attempts to brood her well-feathered nestlings; a fine mistle thrush (centre) feeds its young in the nest; a fieldfare (bottom) shows its subtle markings, the grey head and warm brown back.

on the back and warmer overall colouring. It is not so hardy as its close relative and may become more dependent on man in very cold weather when many of these birds perish.

The song thrush's feeding habits are similar to those of other thrushes except for its remarkable ability to use a kind of tool: a large stone upon which snail shells are broken open.

By comparison with the mistle thrush with its harsh call and the blackbird's noisy clamour, the song thrush goes about its business very quietly, often remaining silent as it hops about the garden in search of food. Its most familiar contribution to the bird sounds in a garden is its much-loved song with its ringing, crystal-clear notes.

MISTLE THRUSH *Turdus viscivorus*

SIZE 265 mm—the largest thrush found in Britain.

STATUS AND DISTRIBUTION Quite common, throughout the year, in all parts of Britain, except remote northern isles.

IN GARDENS Quite common at all times but less so than the song thrush. Occasionally visits bird-tables.

Larger than the song thrush but often confused with it, the mistle thrush may be found in various habitats including farmland, woodland, moorland with scattered trees as well as parks and gardens in towns or even large cities. Compared to the warm browns of the song thrush, this bird is less colourful. The large dark spots are on an almost white breast and throat and its back is a pale grey-brown, giving the bird an overall 'washed-out' appearance. The sexes are alike.

It is easy to identify this bird by its often-heard call—a harsh, rasping rattle, frequently given as the bird flies off. The song, usually given from a tall tree, is not unlike that of both song thrush and blackbird, a fine performance with considerable carrying power. One extraordinary feature of this bird's singing is its habit of singing in rain.

Unlike the song thrush, the mistle thrush is sometimes seen in small flocks, especially in late summer and autumn. In flight it can be taken for a woodpecker, having a similar, undulating flight.

145

REDWING *Turdus iliacus*

SIZE   210 mm—slightly smaller than a song thrush and the smallest of the true thrushes found in Britain.

STATUS AND DISTRIBUTION   A common winter visitor to all parts of Britain; a few breed in northern Scotland.

IN GARDENS   Irregular in mild winters; not uncommon in cold weather, when it may visit bird-tables.

Along with the fieldfare, with which it invariably mixes, the redwing is the most conspicuous winter visitor. In September, October and November, large flocks of both birds appear in many fields across the length and breadth of Britain, having flown south from their breeding grounds in Scandinavia and northern Europe. In cold spells they are even more numerous in the southern half of Britain, moving south and west as the winter hardens and food becomes more difficult to find. At such times, considerable numbers may be seen in and around towns where they feed on any area of short grass which has not frozen too solid: parks, roadside verges and garden lawns. They can become used to the regular passage of cars and pedestrians but this is a species which suffers severely in cold weather so a redwing which only hops rather half-heartedly away from a human is probably hungry and weak rather than tame.

In appearance, the redwing looks very like a slightly small song thrush but can be distinguished by two features which that bird lacks: a white stripe above the eye and an orange-red flank, from which the redwing gains its somewhat inappropriate name, for the wings themselves are not red, except for some feathers on the underside of the wing near the body.

The redwing will come only reluctantly to a bird-table in winter, even when conditions are so bad that many of the flock are dying. But berries will be picked off garden bushes such as holly and cotoneaster, as will fruit and berries scattered on the ground. These will be ignored as soon as the ground thaws sufficiently to enable the birds to probe for worms and insects.

FIELDFARE *Turdus pilaris*

SIZE   250 mm—the same size as a blackbird.

STATUS AND DISTRIBUTION   A common winter visitor to all parts of Britain. Tiny numbers breed in a few northern parts.

IN GARDENS   Infrequent in mild winters; quite common in cold weather in certain gardens. Uncommon in town gardens. Occasionally visits bird-tables.

The movements of flocks of fieldfares in winter are similar to those already described for the red wing, but it is a hardier bird, more able to survive severe wintry weather. It is, therefore, less likely to be driven into towns and suburban gardens to search for food, although gardens close to open country frequently receive visits when berries are plucked from bushes or rotten fruit taken from the ground, especially windfall apples and pears.

The fieldfare is colourful for a thrush, with an attractive combination of light-grey head and rump, chestnut wings and the black spots of the chest and throat placed on a copper background. When seen at a distance in a field, the fieldfares stand out from redwings by their distinctive posture with the long wings slung low, drooping below the body.

A flock of fieldfares flying overhead invariably causes one to look up by their loud repeated 'chak chak' calls.

LESSER SPOTTED WOODPECKER
Dendrocopos minor

SIZE   150 mm—only fractionally larger than a house sparrow.

STATUS AND DISTRIBUTION   Occurs sporadically, mainly in the southern half of England and in Wales; nowhere very plentiful but not uncommon in favoured districts. Present all year round.

IN GARDENS   Unlikely in many gardens but fairly regular in wooded gardens in some areas. Has been known to visit bird-tables.

In colour, this bird is similar to the great spotted woodpecker (white underneath and black and

Because of its small size the lesser spotted woodpecker is easily distinguished from other woodpeckers. The male (top) has a red crown; the female possesses no red markings at all.

white above) but there are some important differences. The male lesser spotted has a red crown, and no other red markings; the female has a white crown and there is no red on her at all. The species lacks the red under-tail coverts of the larger relative. The beak is less woodpecker-like, rather more delicate. The juveniles are duller in colouring and may have red crowns. The back and wings of the lesser spotted woodpecker are boldly barred with white lateral lines, which have given the bird its secondary name of barred woodpecker.

Because of its small size and the fact that it finds much of its food among the topmost branches of large, old trees, the lesser spotted woodpecker is a bird seen only infrequently. In addition, it is far less common than its two bigger relatives and, outside the breeding season, usually silent and, as it does not draw attention to itself, it is regarded as both rare and shy, yet it is neither.

Although it is not a garden bird in that it will not use bird-tables, lawns and nest-boxes, in some suburbs well stocked with mature deciduous trees, the lesser spotted woodpecker may well carry on its normal life in a garden—or, to be more accurate, several gardens—as if the area were merely a wood with clearings, and for the most part man will be disregarded.

For instance, in some parts of the Thames Valley the lesser spotted woodpecker's high-pitched call, 'pee-pee-pee-pee-pee', is a familiar sound in spring. In one suburban garden in Oxfordshire, a pair were observed in two consecutive springs taking turns drumming on a dead poplar only about five metres from a bedroom window, which provided excellent viewing for the watchers. Between bouts of drumming the birds indulged in several display flights within a few metres of human activity.

GREAT SPOTTED WOODPECKER
Dendrocopos major

SIZE   230 mm—slightly smaller than a black-bird.
STATUS AND DISTRIBUTION   A common year-round resident throughout Britain except Ireland

At first glance a young great spotted woodpecker may look like a male lesser spotted. However, it is considerably larger and has pink under-tail feathers, which later turn crimson. It also lacks the white barring on the back, but has large white shoulder patches instead.

and the far north of Scotland. The most wide-spread British woodpecker.

IN GARDENS Fairly common in gardens in wooded suburbs. Regularly visits bird-tables in such areas. Sometimes nests in or close to gardens.

Intermediate in size between the lesser spotted and green woodpeckers, the great spotted wood-pecker is unlikely to be confused with any other bird. The chest, belly, throat and face are a creamy-white; there is a black line joining the beak and back; the upperparts and tail are black with white highlights. Possibly the most visually startling feature is the blood-red patch under the tail. The cock bird has another smaller splash of red on the back of the head, although this is found only in an adult bird. The back of the female's head is black. Just to confuse matters, though, the young birds of both sexes have a red crown extending from front to back. They lose this in late summer as they gain their adult plumage, just as their under-tail coverts change from pale pink to deep crimson.

This species of woodpecker is more catholic in its diet than the other two. As well as various insects and their larvae, it feeds on nuts and seeds, including the seeds from pine cones which are easily extracted. The great spotted wood-pecker makes use of a tool in a very rudimentary way: it chisels out a hole into which it wedges a hazel nut or pine cone, using it as a kind of anvil on which the cone or nut is cracked open. In summer, newly-hatched birds of other species are occasionally devoured; with its powerful bill it is quite capable of forcing an entry into a nest-box to take the young. In winter, scraps of various sorts are taken from bird-tables, and this wood-pecker can match the agility of a blue tit when hanging on to a peanut holder.

The great spotted woodpecker is more common

148

in suburban areas than many suppose, as long as there are sufficient old trees to provide for the bird's basic needs: cover, food and nest-sites. Often it would go undetected but for its loud and unmistakable call—a sharp 'check'.

GREEN WOODPECKER *Picus viridis*

SIZE   320 mm.

STATUS AND DISTRIBUTION   A common year-round resident throughout England and Wales and the southern half of Scotland.

IN GARDENS   Not uncommon in gardens in wooded suburbs, often feeding on lawns.

This, by far the largest of the British woodpeckers, is also the most timid. When encountered in woodland it is often flying off; more often one only knows of its presence by its distinctive call, the 'yaffle' which has given rise to its secondary name. At a distance, the call sounds like some demented human laughing.

The green woodpecker is unmistakable with plumage quite unlike any other British bird: a plain, dull, greenish colour, pale buff-green below and a khaki-green above rather than the lime green with which it is often represented by artists. The red crown adds to its striking appearance. When seen flying away, it gives an impression of being a yellow bird on account of the bright lemon-yellow rump which shows up well when the bird is in flight. Once top-gear has been reached, the bird's flight looks quite easy but this slightly heavy-looking bird makes a somewhat laboured take-off from the ground, with wings that look a little too short for the body. The impression given by the outstretched head and pointed beak is of a bulky green and yellow torpedo. Notice the black moustachial stripe extending from the beak down the side of the face. The female's is solid black, the male's is red and black. On both birds the splendid black and white eye stands out brightly against the black feathering at the side of the face. Young birds are speckled versions of the adults.

The green woodpecker is the only one of the three to regularly feed on the ground on golf-courses, playing fields and suburban lawns. It is not searching for worms but rather probing the ground for insects, particularly ants. Favoured ants' nests are returned to time and time again.

Probably the most extraordinary feature of a woodpecker's anatomy is its exceptionally long, prehensile tongue which can extend up to ten centimetres beyond the end of the beak and can be housed in the head only when coiled up. It can be worked deep into holes and crevices and, because it is covered with a sticky substance, small insects and larvae are caught on it and drawn out. So the green woodpecker feeding on your lawn is not pecking at the ants on the surface. Its tongue is wriggling like a snake through the labyrinth of tiny passageways and chambers which make up the ants' nest. The great spotted woodpecker's tongue has the added facility of a hard spear-like tip with tiny barbs on it. With this it can harpoon grubs and other food items and drag them out of their holes.

COLLARED DOVE *Streptopelia decaocto*

SIZE   280 mm.

STATUS AND DISTRIBUTION   Common year-round resident throughout Britain.

IN GARDENS   Common, even in towns. Visits bird-tables.

Considerably smaller than the pigeons, a pale beige-grey in colour, the upper parts light brown, and sporting a distinct black collar around the back of the neck, the collared dove should be easily identified. It frequently visits bird-tables and regularly breeds in gardens, when the rather boring three-note 'cooing' may become an insistent and irritating sound around the house.

Primarily a seed-eating bird, it will take various scraps from the garden bird-table but it can frighten other smaller birds away—merely because of its bulk, for it is not an aggressive bird.

The collared dove is now a prominent feature of most British towns, frequently seen perching on telephone wires and roof tops. This is a remarkable state of affairs when one considers that only half a century ago this species was absent from most of Europe and as late as 1950 it was unknown in Britain.

FERAL PIGEON *Columba livia*

SIZE   Approximately 330 mm, but variable.
STATUS AND DISTRIBUTION   Common in towns and cities throughout Britain.
IN GARDENS   May visit some town gardens where it sometimes visits bird-tables.

This is the pigeon which gets under your feet in the town centre and shares your packed lunch on the park bench. Not a truly wild species in its own right, it 'lives rough' alongside man in towns and cities, having been domesticated in the past. Its wild ancestor the rock dove is still found nesting colonially on sea cliffs in the west and north of Scotland and around the coasts of Ireland but even in these remote areas some 'pure' birds have interbred with feral escapees from dove-cotes and racing-pigeon lofts.

In town populations there are many variations of pattern and colour, many of which bear little resemblance to the original plumage. Some, however, still resemble the true rock dove very closely with grey colouring, and the two distinct black wing bars and white rump. Ledges on tall buildings provide nest-sites and some cities have huge populations of these birds which can pose a problem when their droppings soil pavements, buildings and monuments.

WOODPIGEON *Columba palumbus*

SIZE   410 mm—the largest pigeon found in Britain.
STATUS AND DISTRIBUTION   A common year-round resident in all parts of Britain.
IN GARDENS   Not uncommon in gardens in some towns and cities but does not often visit bird-tables.

In many rural areas where large numbers are shot, a flock of woodpigeons will rise as one at the mere sight of a distant human and a single bird flying overhead, on sighting a human below, will abruptly veer to left or right to evade the expected blast of shot.

Yet in town parks woodpigeons waddle benignly and confidently among the feral pigeons under the feet of pedestrians and they make regular trips into local gardens. In fact, they can become pests on vegetable patches, doing considerable damage to peas, beans and brassica plants as well as to flowers and buds on fruit trees.

The woodpigeon's appearance is distinctive: it has the typical plump body and small head of the pigeon family and plumage of variable light grey, with a pinky-mauve flush around the chest and throat. The identification features to look for are a shapeless white blotch at the side of the neck, a bold white bar on the upperside of each wing (very obvious in flight) and, on the underside of the tail, which is often fanned out in flight, a thick black bar at the tip. No other pigeon or dove has this combination of features.

The woodpigeon could only be confused with the slightly smaller stock dove, which has similar colouring but, without the white neck and wing patches, looks much more uniformly dull grey.

The two species are often found together in mixed flocks and have similar feeding habits but the stock dove is nowhere as common as the woodpigeon and is rarely seen in gardens.

CUCKOO *Cuculus canorus*

SIZE   330 mm.
STATUS AND DISTRIBUTION   Present throughout the British Isles from mid-April to end of July, though young birds will migrate alone in September.
IN GARDENS   Not common, but will occasionally lay in a robin's or dunnock's nest.

The cuckoo is similar in size to the feral pigeon. The grey upperparts of the adult cuckoo, combined with a white breast with horizontal bars, give it a distinct sparrowhawk look while, in flight, the pointed wings and long tail suggest something of a kestrel. Many experienced birdwatchers have been caught out by the cuckoo, for this reason, and have wrongly identified it as either of those two birds of prey.

Although the cuckoo can be found in almost any habitat, it is more a bird of open country than towns or suburban gardens. It is usually found on farmland, commons, heaths, moorland and hills where there are scattered clumps of trees, bushes and hedges. In many areas, the meadow pipit is the favourite host; at water edges, the reed warbler is usually chosen and in more wooded areas, the dunnock.

In view of the cuckoo's preferences, it is not surprising that the larger country gardens are more likely to receive a visit than small suburban gardens. Yet cuckoos do penetrate to the suburbs and sometimes display considerable audacity. For example, in one suburban garden, a young cuckoo was raised in a robin's nest beside a drive-way which was in regular use and in which cars were usually parked.

We should not be surprised by this, or by any-thing achieved by this remarkable bird. Much of its behaviour is extraordinary by any standards and in many ways it is unique among British birds.

It is the female cuckoo, not the male, that arrives first in spring and it is she who chooses and holds a territory. The species is the only British bird to eat certain hairy caterpillars which

other birds seem to find distasteful. In addition, of course, there is the whole process of laying eggs in other birds' nests which we can all too easily take for granted: the small size of egg (relative to the cuckoo's size); the 'imitation' of the markings and colours of the eggs already in the nest; the extremely short incubation period required for the cuckoo's egg (to ensure that it hatches before the host bird's eggs); and the fiercely insistent food-call of the young cuckoo which compels not only its foster parents to provide food but other parent birds, often of other species, to do so too.

SPARROWHAWK *Accipiter nisus*

SIZE   280–380 mm. Male smaller than female.
STATUS AND DISTRIBUTION   Year-round resident. Anywhere in Britain where there are trees.
IN GARDENS   Fleeting visits. Apart from the tawny owl, the only bird of prey likely to visit.

Even though the sparrowhawk is, in national terms, relatively scarce compared with the kestrel, it is more likely to be seen in gardens though a visit by a sparrowhawk can be a frustrating event. To call it 'fleeting' is an understatement. If a kill is executed the victim will be plucked away so swiftly that the human observer will probably be unable to take it all in immediately. Only when he recalls the event later will he fully appreciate the details of the attack.

The sparrowhawk's hunting involves surprise attack. The favourite method is to fly fast over or past a bush, hedge, tree or fence in the hope of catching some unwary small bird on the other side. Although the average garden landscape is too crowded for the kestrel, the sparrowhawk finds the cluttered assemblage of hedges, fences and buildings much to its liking. Small birds may be taken from garden lawns and bird-tables as the sparrowhawk appears without warning over the garden hedge, from between two houses, or even from behind parked cars, with breathtak-ingly fast flight. The sparrowhawk may be seen, on occasions, skimming low across roads, some-times between moving traffic, in pursuit of a fleeing blackbird, robin or sparrow.

As long as there are plenty of mature trees,

The cuckoo occasionally lays its eggs in garden nests. Here a dunnock is feeding a young cuckoo in a hedge in a garden.

preferably conifers, in the vicinity for roosting, or possibly nesting, the sparrowhawk appears quite capable of surviving in a suburban setting.

KESTREL *Falco tinnunculus*

SIZE   300–360 mm. Male always smaller than female.

STATUS AND DISTRIBUTION: Widespread, resident.
IN GARDENS   Rare. Its hunting technique requires open spaces.

There are few people who do not feel a quickening of the pulse at the sight of a bird of prey, whether it be a golden eagle circling high above a remote Scottish peak, or a kestrel hovering beside a busy road or motorway.

The former is hardly likely to be a candidate for inclusion in anyone's list of garden birds but the kestrel is regularly seen around men's dwellings and places of work. It is not quite the smallest British bird of prey but it is the most common and familiar, as well as being the most adaptable. It is as much at home hunting over a town park as a bleak, windswept hillside or moor.

The best clues to distinguishing the kestrel from the sparrowhawk, with which it is most often confused, lie in its general behaviour rather than in its appearance. The kestrel's hover is a well-nigh infallible means of identification: with rapidly fluttering wings and tail fanned out, it holds itself motionless, often head-on into a strong wind, and scours the ground below for any small insect, mammal or bird. If prey is located, the bird drops vertically with claws outstretched; if not, it slices across the skyline and eases upwards to begin another hover elsewhere. The sparrowhawk never hovers in this way.

The kestrel has the typical long, slim, sharply-pointed wings of the falcon family, whereas the wings of the sparrowhawk are shorter and more rounded; and this is perhaps the most reliable field observation feature. Size is not a good method of distinguishing the two, simply because of the variations within each species. Among hawks and falcons the male is invariably smaller than the female.

In towns, kestrels may be seen in almost any open area: playing fields, golf courses, allotments, railway sidings, industrial estates, car parks and waste ground, but it is rarely to be found in gardens which are too broken up by bushes and fences to suit its hunting technique.

TAWNY OWL *Strix aluco*

SIZE   380 mm.
STATUS AND DISTRIBUTION   The most common of Britain's owls and the only one which regularly haunts towns and gardens. (The other British owls are birds of open farmland, moorland or large pine forests.) It is a year-round resident in Britain except north Scotland and Ireland.
IN GARDENS   Quite common at any time of the year, especially near large trees. Uses nest-boxes, if large enough.

This is the only garden bird which is more heard than seen: unlike some owls which hunt in daylight, the tawny owl (or brown owl, as it is sometimes known) rarely ventures forth before dark and returns to its roost well before dawn. The varied sounds this species utters are loud and piercing so its presence around the garden is usually well advertised. The mythical 'tu-wit, tu-woo' sound is in fact two separate elements of the bird's vocabulary: the 'tu-wit' is a harsh 'ker-vik' call, often given in flight, and the 'tu-woo' a ghostly drawn-out sound. The two different sounds are rarely heard together. The tawny owl is relatively unconcerned about man's activities and can sometimes be heard calling from a tall tree very close to busy traffic.

It is an attractive bird, the plumage showing beautiful subtle shades of light brown and cream, flecked with darker browns. Its flight is effortless, silent and buoyant, its broad wings giving the impression of a larger bird.

BLACK-HEADED GULL *Larus ridibundus*

SIZE   350–380 mm.
STATUS AND DISTRIBUTION   Widespread. Nests in many inland areas throughout Britain, though more commonly in the northern half of the British Isles.

IN GARDENS   Persistent, locally, uncommon else-where.

Few people are likely to find it odd that a gull should be included as a garden bird, for so great has been the explosion in Britain's gull population this century that they are now as frequently seen far inland as on the coast. In fact, in many towns and cities, the huge numbers of gulls are a potential health hazard with their habit of bathing in and roosting on the waters of the local reservoir after hours spent scavenging on the refuse tips in the area or the nearby sewage works.

However, the only gull which habitually enters gardens is the black-headed (although, in a few towns in recent years, the slightly larger common gull has begun to do so too). Indeed, at some bird-tables, black-headed gulls can become a nuisance with their voracious appetites and aggressive nature, quite apart from their repeated raucous cries, so unpleasant to the human ear. Other birds keep well away as the gulls dip and swoop for almost anything edible—as well as some things which are not.

It is probably as a result of its belligerent nature and adaptability that the black-headed gull has been so successful. Although it is the smallest gull regularly seen in the British Isles, it thrives throughout the region and is our most widespread gull. In summer plumage it is easily distinguished by its chocolate-brown head which, incidentally, is never black despite the bird's name. In winter the head is white except for a dark smudge behind the eye. Other distinctive features are the red legs and beak which vary from dark red in summer to bright red in winter. Young birds, which take two years to reach full adult plumage, have patchy brown, grey and black wings, instead of the silvery-grey upper wings of their elders, and a black bar across the end of the tail.

Other species of gull may be seen in towns and cities mainly during autumn and winter, but they are all larger than the black-headed gull and lack the dark head markings and red legs and beak. They are not likely to visit a garden in search of food.

JACKDAW *Corvus monedula*

SIZE   330 mm—considerably smaller than rook or crow.

STATUS AND DISTRIBUTION   Common at all times of the year throughout Britain, except the far north.

IN GARDENS   Not a common visitor, except in gardens near a nesting colony or favoured roost. May nest in chimneys of houses.

Jackdaws nest and roost in colonies, some of which are found in towns and cities. Near these traditional gathering sites, the jackdaw is a common garden visitor, often taking food from a bird-table, although elsewhere there are many gardens in which it is rarely seen. In fact, the jackdaw is more a bird of open country, nesting communally in holes in old trees or even on high sea cliffs.

The jackdaw is much smaller than the other black members of the crow family and so much larger than a blackbird as to make identification straightforward. The neck is light grey giving the black crown considerable prominence in some individuals. It is the only large black bird with a white eye, seen as pale blue close to. The sexes are alike.

The most frequently-heard sound is a loud 'jack', a sharp cutting sound.

JAY *Garrulus glandarius*

SIZE   340 mm.

STATUS AND DISTRIBUTION   A year-round resident throughout most of Britain except far north-west. Quite common.

IN GARDENS   In wooded suburbs or near woods and parks, not uncommon but its visits are irregular. Will visit bird-tables cautiously.

A retiring woodland bird by nature, the jay is the most colourful of the British corvids: it is pale salmon-pink below and chestnut above, and has black, white and azure-blue wings, black tail and white rump. Often all one sees of this bird is its rear view as it hurries away into the trees and, at such times, the combination of the large size and

The three all-black corvids are sometimes confused. The jackdaw (top) is much smaller than the other two and has a distinctive black cap and a white or pale-blue iris. The adult rook (centre) has a white face where no feathers grow. On the face of the crow (bottom) black feathers extend right to the black bill.

very obvious white rump are conclusive signs of its identity. A closer view reveals some striking visual characteristics: white crown spotted with black which, when raised, looks like the bristles of a tiny porcupine, the piercing white and black eye, the black moustachial stripe and the striped black, white and blues on the wing coverts, which are surely among the most beautiful of any bird seen in these islands. The sexes are alike.

Flying looks like hard work to this bird, with its slightly undulating 'flappy' flight and it is a bird which is rarely seen far from trees. The harsh call, when known, is unmistakable, the most tuneless and ear-piercing of sounds, as if some dreadful deed were being perpetrated. It also has a sharp 'ke-vick' sound which can lead the unsuspecting to think that a tawny owl is near.

In common with most of the crow family, the jay has extremely varied tastes and includes in its diet acorns, nuts, fruit, berries, small mammals, birds and insects, birds' eggs and various scraps taken from the garden bird-table or compost heap.

MAGPIE *Pica pica*

SIZE 460 mm—including long tail which accounts for about half of its length.
STATUS AND DISTRIBUTION A year-round resident throughout Britain, except for north of Scotland. Very common.
IN GARDENS Quite common, even in towns and suburbs. Visits bird-tables.

A noisy and showy bird, the magpie is unlikely to go unnoticed. If its call (a mixture of a machine-gun-like rattle and grating laughter) does not catch the ear, then the appearance in your garden of a big, black and white bird with an extremely long tail will catch your eye. The head is all black as are the back and chest; belly and flanks are white, the wings are black and white, the tail black. However, at close quarters, one can see that the black areas have a beautiful, metallic sheen so that in certain lights the wings are dark blue and the tail iridescent green.

In country districts, magpies are very wary of human presence but in some towns and suburbs they have become thoroughly acclimatised to humans and traffic and may demonstrate considerable audacity in a search for food in municipal parks and gardens.

They have a reputation for thieving twinkling objects, not to eat but to place in the nest, although this does not happen as often as one may be led to believe. The diet is extremely varied and includes insects, small mammals, and amphibians, fruit and scraps taken from compost heaps, bird-tables and even refuse tips. Magpies are most efficient in locating other birds' nests and probably devour more eggs and young birds than any other predator.

CARRION CROW *Corvus corone corone*
ROOK *Corvus frugilegus*

SIZE   460 mm—larger than any other garden bird.

STATUS AND DISTRIBUTION   Common year-round residents throughout Britain, except that the hooded crow replaces the carrion crow in Ireland and north-west Scotland. The rook is absent from parts of northern Scotland.

IN GARDENS   Carrion crow occasionally occurs, and sometimes visits bird-tables. Rook rarely alights in gardens, often seen flying overhead.

Virtually identical in appearance, the crow and rook are best distinguished by the beak and the area around it. The crow's face is black and its beak dark grey; the rook's beak is pale and, because there is an area of unfeathered pale skin at the base of the beak, it appears to have a white face. In addition, the rook's flank feathers are very thick, as if it is wearing rather voluminous, black plus-fours. This diagnostic feature is important where a young rook is concerned because the juveniles of the species lack the white face, thus looking more like a crow.

The crow is much more versatile in its haunts, being found in habitats from sea-cliffs and hill-country to towns and suburbs. Park litter bins are raided, roads are picked clean of squashed animal life and rubbish tips are scoured for edible waste. Some town gardens are visited, with the crow scavenging around compost heaps or, occasionally, dropping down onto the bird-table to seize the largest scraps available.

The rook is a bird of open farmland where it feeds in flocks on the ground, nesting in groups of tall trees in rookeries which vary from three or four nests to fifty or more. These are usually found in villages or on the edge of small towns close to agricultural land and are not infrequently sited in the gardens of large country houses though the rook will disregard gardens for the most part, and is described here for comparison with the carrion crow with which it is so often confused.

APPENDIX
CONSERVATION BODIES

Royal Society for the Protection of Birds (RSPB)

The Lodge, Sandy, Bedfordshire SG19 2DL

A model conservation organisation, the RSPB carries out magnificent work on 78 reserves, undertakes programmes of research, education, bird protection and law-enforcement and fights pollution and destruction of valuable habitat. There are over 150 local members' groups throughout the country which meet regularly for birdwatching excursions, lectures and film shows. Its junior branch, The Young Ornithologists' Club (YOC), caters for birdwatchers up to the age of 15.

The combined membership for the two bodies is nearly half a million. Both exist by voluntary contributions, members' subscriptions and profits from sales of goods and film-making.

The British Trust for Ornithology (BTO)

Beech Grove, Tring, Hertfordshire HP23 5NR

Smaller than the RSPB, the BTO is an organisation for the serious birdwatcher. It does not own or manage reserves but is responsible for outstanding work: bird population studies, nest records, ringing and many other areas of research. It also produces some excellent informative and helpful publications such as *The Atlas of Breeding Birds in Britain and Ireland* and the *Nestboxes* booklet.

The Society for the Promotion of Nature Conservation (SPNC)

The Green, Nettleham, Lincoln LN2 2NR

There are numerous local natural history groups throughout Britain. In fact, there can hardly be any part of Britain which is not represented by at least one such organisation. Details of many of these can be obtained from the above address. The SPNC also has a junior branch, called WATCH, for members up to the age of 14.

The Nature Conservancy Council

Northminster House, Peterborough PE1 1UA

This is the government body which promotes nature conservation in Great Britain.

Information about other organisations, including small, local ornithological groups, is usually available at local museums, libraries or town halls.

BIBLIOGRAPHY

Armstrong, E. A., *The Wren* (Collins, London 1955)

Bannerman, D. A., *The Birds of the British Isles* (12 vols.) (Oliver and Boyd, London 1954)

Barrington, R., *The Bird Gardener's Book* (Wolfe, London 1971)

Bennett, L., *RSPB Book of Garden Birds* (Hamlyn, London 1978)

Batten L., Flegg J. J. M., et al, *Birdwatchers' Year* (Poyser, Berkhamstead 1973)

Brown, L., *British Birds of Prey* (Collins, London 1976)

Bruun, B., *Birds of Britain and Europe* (Hamlyn, London 1971)

Buxton, J., *The Redstart* (Collins, London 1950)

Campbell, B., *The Oxford Book of Birds* (Oxford, London 1964)

Chinery, M., *The Natural History of the Garden* (Collins, London 1977)

Committee on Bird Sanctuaries in the Royal Parks, *Bird Life in the Royal Parks 1975, 1976* (Dept. of the Environment, London 1977, 1978)

Coombs, F., *The Crows* (Batsford, London 1978)

Coward, T. A., edited by Barnes J. A. G., *Birds of the British Isles and their Eggs* (Frederick Warne, London 1969)

Fisher, J., revised Flegg J. J. M., *Watching Birds* (Poyser, Berkhamsted 1974)

Fitter, R. S. R., *London's Natural History* (Collins, London 1945)

Fitter, R. S. R. and Richardson, R. A., *Collins Pocket Guide to British Birds* (Collins, London 1952)

Flegg, J. J. M. and Glue, D. E., *Nestboxes* (British Trust for Ornithology, Tring 1971)

Goodwin, D., *Birds of Man's World* (Cornell University Press, London 1978)

Harrison, C., *A Field Guide to the Nests, Eggs and Nestlings of European Birds* (Collins, London 1975)

Hayman, P and Burton, P., *The Birdlife of Britain* (Mitchell Beazley, London 1976)

Heinzel, H., Fitter, R. S. R. and Parslow, J., *The Birds of Britain and Europe* (Collins, London 1972)

Hickin, N. E., *Bird Nest-Boxing* (Stanley Paul, London 1971)

Hollom, P. A. D., *The Popular Handbook of British Birds* (Witherby, London 1962)

Hudson, R., *Early and Late Dates for Summer Migrants* (BTO, Tring 1973)

Johns, C. A., *British Birds in their Haunts* (Routledge, London 1909)

Lack, D., *The Life of the Robin* (Witherby, London 1965)

Lack, D., *Swifts in a Tower* (Methuen, London 1956)

Lack, D., *Population Studies of Birds* (Oxford, London 1966)

Lockley, R. M., *The Naturalist in Wales* (David and Charles, Newton Abbot 1970)

Mabey, R., *The Unofficial Countryside* (Collins, London 1973)

Murton, R. K., *Man and Birds* (Collins, London 1971)

Murton, R. K., *The Woodpigeon* (Collins, London 1965)

Newton, I., *Finches* (Collins, London 1972)

Parslow, J., *Breeding Birds of Britain and Ireland* (Poyser, London 1973)

Perrins, C., *British Tits* (Collins, London 1979)

Perrins, C., *Birds* (Collins, London 1974)

Peterson, R., Mountfort, G., and Hollom, P. A. D., *A Field Guide to Birds of Britain and Europe* (Collins, London 1954)

Reade, W., and Hosking, E., *Nesting Birds, Eggs and Fledglings* (Blandford Press, London 1967)

Sharrock, J. T. R. (compiled on behalf of the British Trust for Ornithology and Irish Wildbird Conservancy), *The Atlas of Breeding Birds in Britain and Ireland* (Poyser, London 1976)

Sielmann, H., *My Year with the Woodpeckers* (translation) (Barrie and Rockliff, London 1959)

Simms, E., *British Thrushes* (Collins, London 1978)

Simms, E., *Woodland Birds* (Collins, London 1971)

Simms, E., *Birds of Town and Suburb* (Collins, London 1975)

Snow, D. W., *A Study of Blackbirds* (Allen & Unwin, London 1958)

Soper, T., *The New Bird Table Book* (David and Charles, Newton Abbot 1965)

Sparks, J., and Soper, T., *Owls: Their Natural and Unnatural History* (David and Charles, Newton Abbot 1970)

Summers-Smith, J. D., *The House Sparrow* (Collins, London 1963)

Turner, E. L., *Every Garden a Bird Sanctuary* (Witherby, London 1935)

White, G., *The Natural History of Selborne* (first published 1789) (Shepheard-Walwyn, London 1978)

Wilmore, S. B., *Crows, Jays, Ravens and Their Relatives* (David and Charles, London 1977)

Witherby, H. F., Jourdain, F. C. R., Ticehurst, N. F., Tucker, B. W., *The Handbook of British Birds* (5 vols.) (Witherby, London 1949)

Woldhek, S., *Bird Killing in the Mediterranean* (Report published by the European Committee for the Prevention of Mass Destruction of Migratory Birds, 1979, revised 1980)

Yapp, W. B., *Birds and Woods* (Oxford, London 1962)

Young, J. Z., *The Life of Vertebrates* (Oxford, London 1962)

PICTURE CREDITS

INDEX

Figures in **bold** refer to illustrations